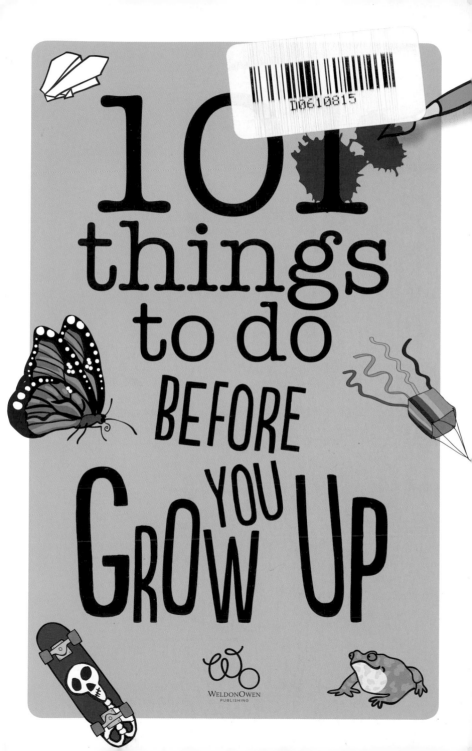

101 things to do BEFORE YOU GROW UP

WELDONOWEN
PUBLISHING

WELDONOWEN
PUBLISHING

First published in Great Britain by
Weldon Owen
Deepdene Lodge
Deepdene Avenue
Dorking RH5 4AT, UK

www.weldonowen.co.uk
www.bonnierpublishing.com

ISBN: 978-1-78342-077-3

Printed in Turkey

101 things to do BEFORE YOU GROW UP

CONTENTS

1 LAUNCH A PLASTIC-BAG PARACHUTE

It's a bird. It's a plane. It's... a plastic bag!
Send your toys flying with this cool parachute.

YOU WILL NEED:

- Plastic bag or light material
- Scissors
- Needle and 4 pieces of thread – about 50cm each
- Masking tape
- 4 paper clips
- Small object to act as the weight (a little action figure would be perfect)
- Rubber band

1 Cut out a large square from your plastic bag or material and add tape to all four corners on the top and the bottom (8 pieces in total).

2 Thread your needle and push it through one corner, then tie the ends to a paper clip. Repeat for all corners.

3 Make a harness for your figure. Wrap a rubber band around it as shown, then hook onto your paper clips.

4 Find a safe high spot to drop your parachute from, and watch your action figure float to the ground.

DONE!   DATE COMPLETED

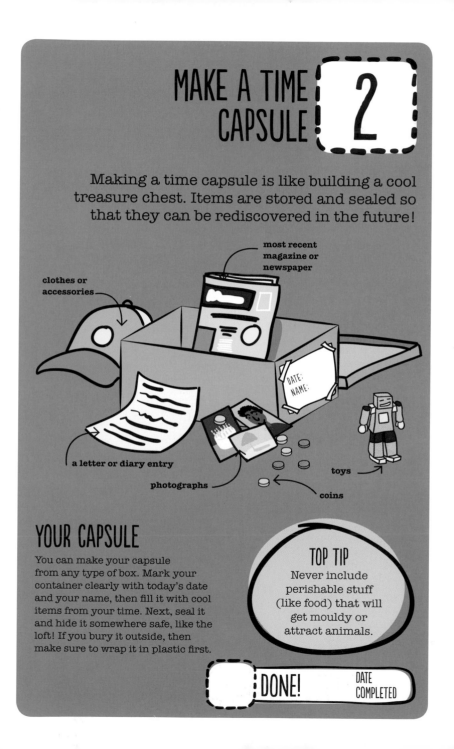

MAKE A TIME CAPSULE

Making a time capsule is like building a cool treasure chest. Items are stored and sealed so that they can be rediscovered in the future!

most recent magazine or newspaper

clothes or accessories

DATE:
NAME:

a letter or diary entry

photographs

toys

coins

YOUR CAPSULE

You can make your capsule from any type of box. Mark your container clearly with today's date and your name, then fill it with cool items from your time. Next, seal it and hide it somewhere safe, like the loft! If you bury it outside, then make sure to wrap it in plastic first.

TOP TIP
Never include perishable stuff (like food) that will get mouldy or attract animals.

DONE!

DATE COMPLETED

3 LEARN TO JUGGLE THREE OBJECTS

Juggling is the perfect skill for showing off. With just a little focus, practice and rhythm, you can be the life of any party!

SAFETY FIRST!

First things first: the primary rule of juggling is safety. So don't even THINK about juggling flaming torches! Learn to juggle with small beanbags or balls. With the right objects, and the right technique, you'll be ready to toss and twirl in no time at all – and look mighty cool doing it!

1 Grab a small ball or beanbag. Throw it from hand to hand in an arc. Toss it so that it's level with your eyes.

HANDY TO KNOW!

One of your hands is called the dominant hand because it does most of the throwing and catching. It's usually the hand you write with.

2 Throw the ball from one hand to the other without reaching out to grab the ball. Practise until you've got a good rhythm.

3 Now try tossing two balls at once. As the first ball is coming down, throw the second ball and catch both.

4 Now add a third ball, so you are holding three balls in total. Your dominant hand should be holding two.

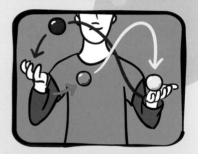

5 Throw the first two balls just as before, holding the third ball in your dominant hand.

6 Add a third throw just when the second ball is at its peak and keep throwing the balls in a continuous loop.

WHY NOT?
Substitute one of the balls for an apple. During the juggle, try to take a bite from the apple!

DONE!   DATE COMPLETED

4 COUNT TO TEN IN FIVE DIFFERENT LANGUAGES

Thousands of languages are spoken across the globe. Impress your mates by counting to ten in five of them!

According to linguists (people who study languages) 6,909 languages are spoken in the world. Yikes! Study the numbers 1 to 10 in the chart below (how to pronounce them is in brackets). Impress your family and teachers with your linguistic know-how!

	1	2	3	4	5	6	7	8	9	10
English	One	Two	Three	Four	Five	Six	Seven	Eight	Nine	Ten
French	Un (uh)	Deux (duhr)	Trois (twah)	Quatre (katr)	Cinq (sank)	Six (sees)	Sept (set)	Huit (weet)	Neuf (nurf)	Dix (dees)
Mandarin Chinese	Yi (eee)	Er (arr)	San (sahn)	Si (ssuh)	Wu (woo)	Liu (liou)	Qi (chee)	Ba (bah)	Jiu (Jeou)	Shi (shehr)
Spanish	Uno (oono)	Dos (dose)	Tres (tress)	Cuatro (kwah-tro)	Cinco (sink-oh)	Seis (sayss)	Siete (syet-tah)	Ocho (oh-cho)	Nueve (nwehv-ay)	Diez (dees)
Russian	Adin (ah-din)	Dva (dvah)	Tri (tree)	Chetyre (che-terr-ee-eh)	Pyat' (pyah-ts)	Shyest' (shey-st)	Cyem (siem)	Voysy-em (vo-siem)	Dyevy-et (dee-eviet)	Dyeset (de-ee-siet)

✓ DONE! 27 Aug DATE 2020 COMPLETED

TELL THE TIME WITHOUT A CLOCK!

A sundial uses the sun to measure the passing of time by casting a shadow over numbers. How cool?!

YOU WILL NEED:
- Large polystyrene or paper drinking cup, with a plastic lid and straw
- Watch or clock
- Permanent marker
- Pencil
- Tape
- Some small pebbles (enough to fill the cup about half full)
- Compass (see activity 12)

plastic lid

straw

tape

cup

1 Use the pencil to poke a hole in the side of the cup, approximately 5cm below the top. Put the pebbles in the cup so it doesn't tip over. Put the lid on the cup.

2 Put the straw through the hole in the lid and the hole in the side of the cup. Let it stick out about 2cm from the side and tape the straw to the cup.

3 Find a sunny spot and place the cup on a level surface. Use a compass to find north and point the straw in that direction. Make sure that the sun shines right on the straw!

4 At 10am, mark where the shadow from the straw falls on the lid of the cup. Repeat this every hour until 3pm. The next day, you'll be able to tell the time without a clock!

DONE!

DATE COMPLETED

6 GET TIED UP IN KNOTS (OR AT LEAST TIE A FEW)

Here's the thing about knots: they are NOT uncommon. We use knots for tons of things in our daily lives, so learning how to tie one is very important. Here are three useful and easy knots for you to try.

SQUARE KNOT

The square knot is used to tie two ropes together.

1 Lay the left hand end of one rope over the right hand end of the other. Pass the left hand end under the other rope and pull it to the top.

2 Point the ends inwards. Pass the right hand one over the left, then take it down behind it and up to the front through the loop which has now been formed.

3 Pull the knot tight. To remember this knot say: 'left over right and right over left'.

BOWLINE (PRONOUNCED 'BO-LIN')

The bowline is used to form a non-slip loop in the
end of a rope. It was traditionally a waist knot
used by climbers before harnesses were used.

1 Form a loop in the
rope by passing
the working
(bottom) part of
your rope up over
the standing part
(the attached part).

2 Pass the working end
back up through the
loop from behind and
then around the back of
the standing part.

3 Pass the working
end back down the
loop and pull tight.

CLOVE HITCH

Use this to tie a rope to a rail.

1 Pass the working
end over and
under a rail or
post. Run it across
the standing part.

2 Go round the rail
again, bringing the
working end back.
Tuck it under the cross.

3 Pull tight. The
two ends of the
rope should lay
next to each other
under the cross, in
opposite directions.

DONE! DATE COMPLETED

7 SEND A MESSAGE IN A BOTTLE

What if you wrote a note, stuck it into a bottle and tossed it into the ocean? How far would it go? Who would find it? See for yourself!

1 Find a medium-sized bottle with a strong lid to keep the water out.

2 Find some thin card, if you can, and a permanent marker to write your note.

3 Write your message. Include an adult's email address so that whoever finds the bottle can contact you!

4 Make sure the tide is on its way out when you throw your bottle into the sea, otherwise it will just end up back on land. Off it goes!

DONE!   DATE COMPLETED

Build a wall of ice to hide your snowballs – then get ready for a real winter battle.

FOR THE WALL:

Using a rectangular tub (like an ice-cream tub), scoop snow, pack it down and then release it as 'snow bricks'. As a stand-out special effect, decorate your wall with snow that's been mixed with food colouring.

FOR THE BALLS:

- Find perfect snow. You don't want snow too wet or you'll have slushballs instead of snowballs.

- Be careful when packing snowballs that you don't mix in twigs, rocks or too much ice. You'll often find perfect snowball snow closer to a curb or house where there's more heat – the snow will have melted a teeny bit.

- Frostbite alert! Wear warm gloves to pack and roll your snowballs. Don't bare-hand it.

- Aha! Your icy wall provides the perfect place to build up a stockpile. The ultimate snowball launch is firing 2 or 3 in a row. Splat! Your enemy won't know what hit 'em.

GUESS WHAT?
In January 2013, 5,800 people had a full-on 'snowbrawl' fight in Seattle, USA.

DONE!

DATE COMPLETED

9 MAKE THE ULTIMATE PIZZA

Eating a pizza is even better when it's got all your favourite toppings – so why not make one yourself!

SAFETY FIRST

Ask an adult to help you put your pizza in the oven and take it out again.

1 For the quickest pizza, head to your supermarket and look for pre-made pizza bases. Preheat the oven as instructed on the packet.

2 Place your base flat on a pizza stone or a baking sheet (that's been drizzled with a bit of oil first).

3 Spoon out some sauce (made from tinned tomatoes and a sprinkling of basil). Add mozzarella or cheddar cheese on top.

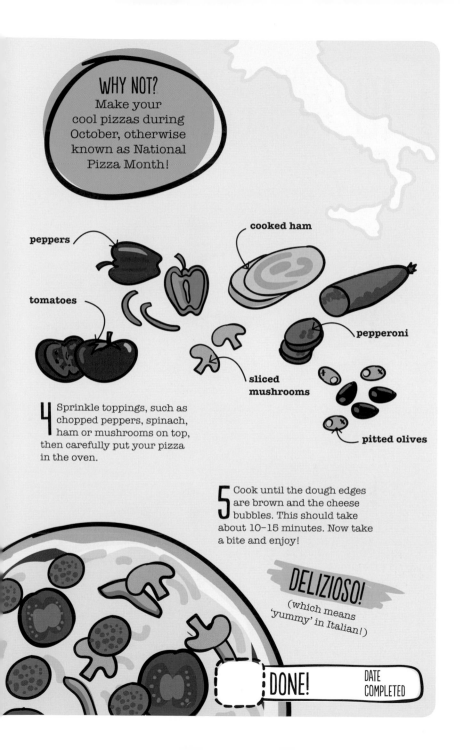

WHY NOT?
Make your cool pizzas during October, otherwise known as National Pizza Month!

peppers

cooked ham

tomatoes

pepperoni

sliced mushrooms

pitted olives

4 Sprinkle toppings, such as chopped peppers, spinach, ham or mushrooms on top, then carefully put your pizza in the oven.

5 Cook until the dough edges are brown and the cheese bubbles. This should take about 10–15 minutes. Now take a bite and enjoy!

DELIZIOSO!
(which means 'yummy' in Italian!)

DONE!

DATE COMPLETED

10 COME UP WITH A SECRET HANDSHAKE

Psssst! What's the coolest way for best friends to say hi? A super-secret handshake, complete with tugs, snaps and other slick moves.

WHOOP-WHOOP!

1.
2.
3.

1 Decide on five or six moves for the handshake. Check out the list below, and see what works for you and your pals.

2 Any secret handshake should involve all your senses. Add hoots, whistles, tongue-clicks and a shriek or two.

3 Make an order for your handshake steps. Remember to add in something unique to your handshake – a move you think of together.

WHY NOT TRY...

- Fist bump
- Clasp
- Pinky swear
- Touch fingertips
- Shoulder bump
- Fingers in the air
- Itsy Bitsy Spider fingertips
- High fives (up high and down low)
- High tens (that's with both hands)
- Hug it out
- Hip check
- Palm swipe
- Finger pulls

REMEMBER
Practise, practise, PRACTISE. You may have five or more steps in the shake, but you want to make it look effortless.

DONE!   DATE COMPLETED

DRAW A SELF-PORTRAIT

A self-portrait is when the artist paints himself or herself. Look at yourself in a mirror, grab a pen and paper and start your own!

1 To start your portrait, map out your features. Your hand is about as large as your face, so put your hand on the page.

2 Mark the top finger with a dot and then the heel of your palm with another dot. Connect them with an oval shape.

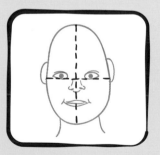

3 Draw a dotted cross inside the oval. Eyes sit on top of the horizontal line, the nose is at the centre and your mouth is below that.

4 Add more details, such as eyebrows, ears and hair. Then erase the dotted cross and... voilà! You have a portrait!

DONE! DATE COMPLETED

12 MAKE YOUR OWN COMPASS

A compass is a tool for navigation. It contains a magnetised needle that responds to our planet's magnetism and points NORTH.

YOU WILL NEED:

- Straightened paper clip to use as a needle
- Bar magnet (a straight rectangular magnet with a north and south pole on either side)
- Pliers
- Round piece of cork
- Small dish half-filled with water

1 Magnetise your paper clip needle by rubbing it against the magnet about 20 times, in the same direction.

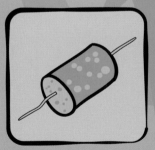

2 Using pliers, carefully push your needle through the cork. You need the same amount of needle showing on each side.

3 Place the cork and needle on the water. The end of the needle that points towards the sun at midday is pointing south if you are in the Northern Hemisphere, and north if you are in the Southern Hemisphere.

DONE! | DATE COMPLETED

WRITE A SPOOKY STORY

You know how to write an essay for school and diary entries are easy, but what do you know about writing a story that scares? Here are four tips to make your next tale a real scream.

Start by scaring the pants off yourself. Face your fears head-on. What kind of story would make your toes curl? What do you see in your scariest dreams? Write about THAT.

What?

Choose a 'what if' and go from there. What if you got locked out after dark? What if you faced a beast in the woods? What if your best friend was a vampire?

Where?

Choose a setting and add loads of scary details: fog, strange sounds, darkness and more. Maybe make it so cold you can see your breath. Brrr!

Who?

Identify the main character. Who is he or she? Why are they in this scary setting? Make up your villain. What do they look like? How does he or she act? Identify three moments of danger between them and your hero.

How?

Use the right words to scare your reader, such as 'ghoulish', 'terrifying' or 'spooky'. Take your time to present the details. Remember that half the work is creating tension! Tell the reader that bad things will happen – and then write them... eventually.

DONE!

DATE COMPLETED

14 GO STAR GAZING!

Constellations are groups of stars in the night sky. There are at least 88 different constellations, each named after animals or characters from mythology.

WHERE ARE YOU?

The biggest constellation is called Orion, also known as The Great Hunter. How can you find it? Go outside in the evening and look at the southwest sky if you are in the Northern Hemisphere, or the northwestern sky if you are in the Southern Hemisphere. If you live on or near the equator, Orion is visible in the western sky.

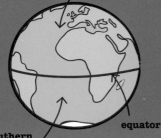

Northern Hemisphere

equator

Southern Hemisphere

Plough

URSA MAJOR

A famous constellation is Ursa Major, or the Great Bear. Inside Ursa Major is the Plough, also called the Big Dipper. But guess what? The Plough is NOT a constellation. It is actually called an 'asterism', which is a grouping of stars within the larger constellation.

ORION

Look for the pattern of stars shown here (turn this page upside down if you are looking from the Southern Hemisphere). Three bright stars close together in a line are easiest to spot first. These three stars represent Orion's belt. Two bright stars above this are Orion's shoulders. The two below are his knees.

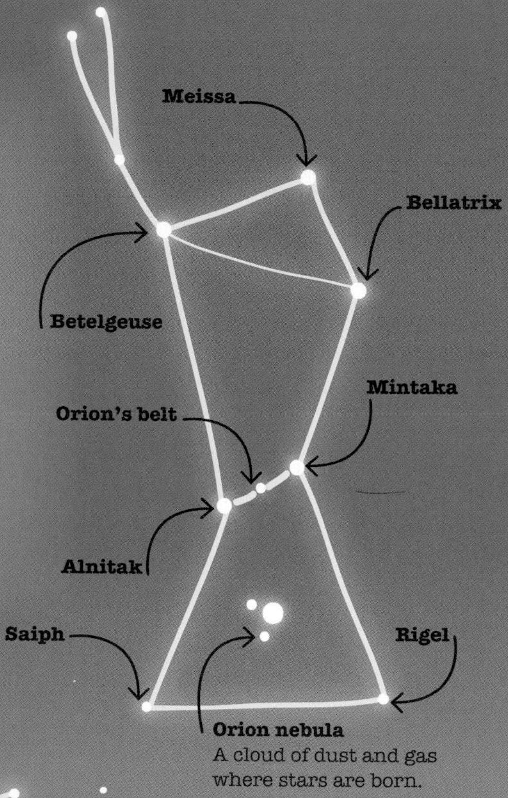

Meissa

Bellatrix

Betelgeuse

Mintaka

Orion's belt

Alnitak

Saiph

Rigel

Orion nebula
A cloud of dust and gas where stars are born.

CANIS MINOR

CANIS MAJOR

Near Orion you may be able to see Canis Major and Canis Minor, Orion's two hunting dog companions.

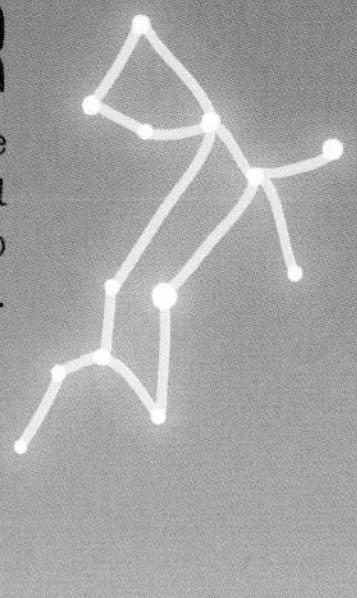

WHY NOT?
Find out when you can see a meteor shower near you and spot a shooting star!

DONE!

DATE COMPLETED

15 BE A MYTH BUSTER

Put rumours to rest. Forget those superstitions. It's time to bust four popular myths!

Lightning NEVER strikes twice.

Although it seems unlikely, lightning can strike in the same spot more than once. The Empire State Building in New York City has more than 100 lightning strikes every year!

Touch a toad and you'll get WARTS.

Give that toad a break. Just because his skin is covered in bumps doesn't mean you'll catch warts if you touch him. Actually, his bumps are for camouflage!

Bulls get mad when they see the colour RED.

Bullfighters wave a small red cape to get a bull's attention. But believe it or not, it's not the colour of the cape that matters to the bull. It's the movement of the fabric. In fact, bulls are colour-blind, so don't see the colour red the same way you or I would.

If you swallow chewing gum, it takes SEVEN YEARS to digest.

Food we chew and swallow is broken down by enzymes in the digestive system. But here's the problem with gum: its basic ingredient is designed not to break down when chewed. If swallowed, it may take a little extra time to digest... but not seven years!

✓ DONE! 27th Aug DATE 2020 COMPLETED

MAKE SOME MAGIC

Hey presto! The easiest way to impress friends and family is by having a few tricks up your sleeve. Try this one at your next party.

THE FLOATING KETCHUP

Before you start, empty a plastic bottle and fill with water almost all the way to the top.

1 Explain to your audience that you can make a tomato ketchup sachet move at your command, then open the bottle and insert the sachet. Close the lid.

2 With one hand, hold the bottle by the side so you can clearly see the ketchup packet. With the other hand, point at the sachet, giving it commands as you go: 'Ketchup up!', 'Ketchup down!'

3 The trick: as you tell the packet to move, you gently squeeze on the bottle. The water pressure will make the ketchup packet rise and fall and even stop on command!

DONE!   DATE COMPLETED

17 MAKE SPOOKY BLACK FLOWERS

These flowers will look awesome displayed at Halloween, and they're super-simple to make.

YOU WILL NEED:

- White flowers (carnations or roses work well)
- Scissors
- Vase
- Black food colouring

1 Take your flowers and carefully snip off the end of the stems.

2 Fill a vase around 1/3 full of tap water, then add four to five drops of food colouring. You can use any colour, but black is perfect for Halloween!

3 Place your flowers into the vase and leave them for a few hours, or overnight if you can. The flowers will soak up the black water and dye the petals black. Spooky!

WHY NOT?
Forgot flowers for Mother's Day? Use this technique to dye celery sticks. Try pink food colouring instead of black!

MULTI-COLOURED FLOWERS

Once you've mastered this technique, try making two-coloured flowers. Cut the stem into two halves with your scissors and place each half in a different coloured water and food colouring mixture. The petals will soak up both colours separately!

DONE! DATE COMPLETED

18 BRING UP A BUTTERFLY

From egg to adult, butterflies undergo an amazing transformation known as metamorphosis. If you're lucky, you might just see this happen!

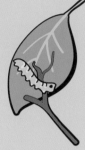

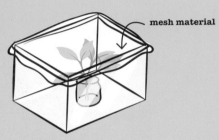

mesh material

1 Make a home for your caterpillar. Use a transparent box and cover it with mesh fabric (a fabric with tiny holes in), so that there's something for the caterpillar to hang on to.

2 Find the caterpillar for you and invite it onto a stick. As you take it, pick up a few leaves from the same plant. It will need these for food!

chrysalis

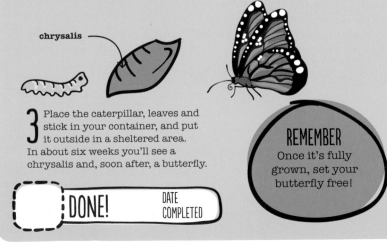

3 Place the caterpillar, leaves and stick in your container, and put it outside in a sheltered area. In about six weeks you'll see a chrysalis and, soon after, a butterfly.

REMEMBER
Once it's fully grown, set your butterfly free!

DONE!   DATE COMPLETED

PLAY WITH SHADOW PUPPETS

You can make an entire zoo come to life on your wall, just using your hands, fingers and some clever lighting.

SHOWTIME!

Shine a torch onto an empty wall. The fun of making animal shadow puppets is the practice! Try different shapes and animals to see what looks best.

goat

alligator

rabbit

camel

bird

WHY NOT?
Put on a shadow puppet show for your friends and family!

DONE!

DATE COMPLETED

20 DRAW A COMIC STRIP

Comic strips can be funny, thoughtful or packed with adventure! Here are some important pointers to help you draw your own.

1 Figure out what your style will be when you write and draw your comic. If you don't care so much about the details, that's okay! Draw stick figures and come up with clever punchlines or a silly drawing.

2 Draw your ideas in pencil first, so that you can make adjustments as you go along.

3 Invent cool characters. Name them and give them simple and distinct features like funky glasses, big hair or scary teeth. What are their best and worst qualities? Funny comic strips need to end with a punchline, adventure strips might end on a cliffhanger!

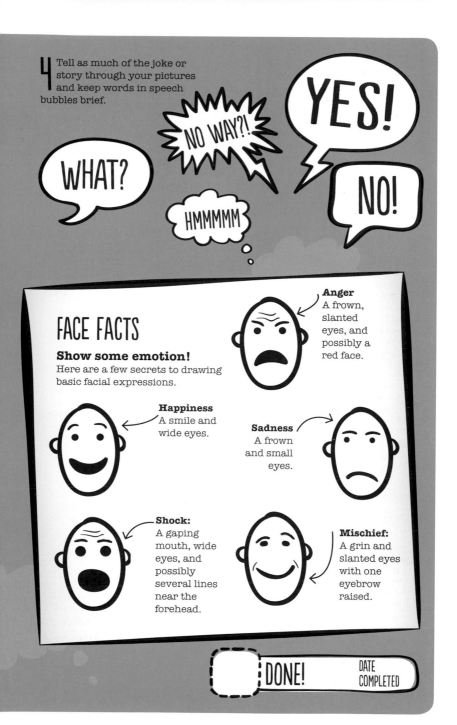

21 MAKE TWO NATURAL INSTRUMENTS

The best music comes from outdoors, like birds chirping or insects buzzing. Make these two instruments to get back to nature!

YOU WILL NEED:

- Cardboard tube
- Paint or coloured markers
- Sticky tape
- Paper
- Plastic or wooden cocktail sticks
- Scissors
- Dried beans

RAIN STICK

The rain stick is a musical instrument from South America usually made from the wooden skeleton of a cactus. Your rain stick will be a little different, but it should produce the same effect.

1 Take a cardboard tube (a kitchen towel or wrapping paper tube works well) and decorate the outside with paint, markers, etc. Tape a circle of paper over one end.

2 Poke some wooden or plastic toothpicks into the tube, following a downward spiral pattern. You should end up with something a lot like the image below. Secure the ends of the sticks with tape.

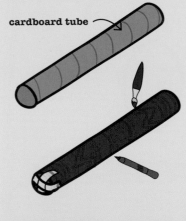

cardboard tube

cocktail sticks

3 Drop a handful of dried beans inside. Then tape another circle of paper over the open end. Tip your stick gently back and forth to hear the soft sound of rain.

dried beans

GRASS TRUMPET

Make a funny, high-pitched squeal to, erm, DELIGHT your friends with just a blade of grass and your hands!

1 Find a wide blade of grass. Hold up your left hand in a loose fist with your thumbnail pointing towards you. Then put your right hand up next to your left hand with the blade of grass flat between your thumbs.

2 Hold the grass between your thumbs. Move the grass so that it is stretched tightly in the gap between your thumbs – and then move the gap against your lips.

3 Pucker your lips as if you were going to blow out a candle and blow hard into the gap. If you do it correctly you will hear the grass make a loud, squeaky sound.

DONE!

DATE COMPLETED

22 INVENT YOUR OWN SUPERHERO

Flash! Zap! Pow! Use your very own superhero in a comic or for your next fancy dress costume. Here are five things every superhero needs.

1 Motivation! There can be no superhero without conflict. What motivates your superhero to dress up and fight evil?

HELP!

2 An identity – or two! Give them a name that reflects their talents and strength. Then come up with a daytime disguise!

3 A costume to fit the identity. A helmet, horns or an oversized mask? A cape? A super-cool symbol?

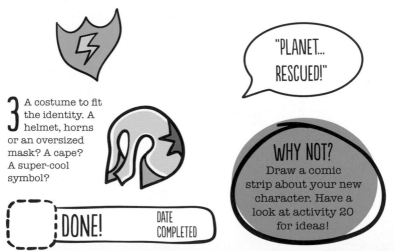

DONE!

DATE COMPLETED

4 The villain! Someone to fight battles with — and launch a sneak attack to take over the world.

5 A tragic flaw and a trademark! Their flaw is the one thing that can defeat them. The trademark could be something the hero says.

"PLANET... RESCUED!"

WHY NOT?
Draw a comic strip about your new character. Have a look at activity 20 for ideas!

Reading music can be like reading a foreign language. Here are some basic tips to help you read notes and the speeds they are played at.

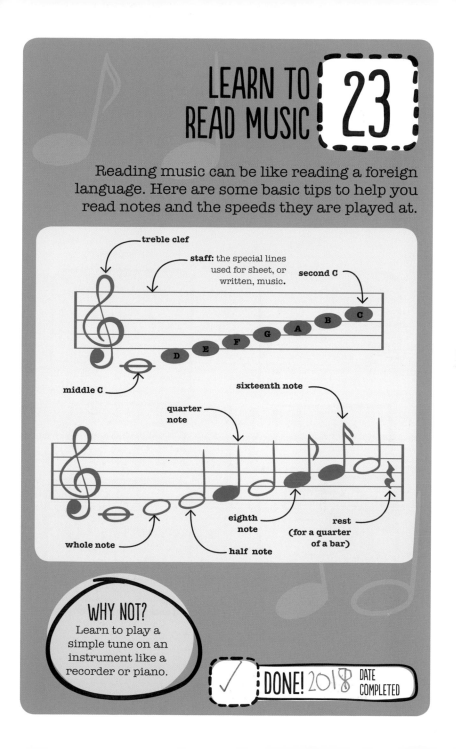

DONE! 2018 DATE COMPLETED

24 MAKE ROCK CANDY

There's nothing better than a science experiment you can eat! You'll definitely be sweet on this treat.

YOU WILL NEED:
- 400ml water
- 800g sugar
- Pencil
- String
- Food colouring
- Lemon juice
- Glass jar

1 Tie a piece of string around the middle of your pencil.

2 The string should be long enough that it almost reaches the bottom when the pencil is placed over the top of the jar.

3 Ask an adult to help you carefully bring the water to the boil and add 100g of the sugar.

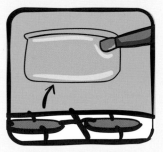

4 When the mixture starts to bubble, begin adding the rest of the sugar, 100g at a time. Once done, take the pan off the heat.

5 Add a couple of drops of food colouring to your mixture and a squeeze of lemon for flavour, then pour into the jar, almost to the top. Place the pencil over the jar and let the string dangle into the liquid. Don't let it settle on the bottom or sides.

6 Find a safe place to leave your jar (not the fridge) and after a day or so, you should start to see crystals forming around the string. Leave it for several days until more crystals form, then leave to dry before enjoying your sweet treat!

final rock candy crystal

REMEMBER

Do not mess around with the jar or put your fingers in it. This disrupts the forming process of the crystalline structure!

WHY NOT?
Indian rock candy is mixed with fennel as a mouth freshener! What will you add to yours?

DONE! DATE COMPLETED

25 DANCE TILL YOU DROP

Practise boogying in front of a mirror, then show off your skills in the ultimate dance off!

1 If there's one dance everyone tries, it's the limbo. A pole or broom is placed up high while the dancers shimmy underneath. Gradually the pole gets lower and lower... how low can you go?

2 Freestyle it! Dancers take it in turns to show off their best moves in the centre of a circle. Try twisting, jumping up and down and body-rolling!

3 Learn a line dance. Get your pals in a line and see who can master the steps to an easy group dance such as the Macarena. Or make up your own line dance!

DONE!   DATE COMPLETED

HARNESS THE POWER OF THE SUN!

Using a simple box on a hot day, you can focus the sun's energy and make an oven that will cook a gooey tasty treat!

YOU WILL NEED:

- Shoe box
- Tin foil
- Cling film
- Glue stick
- Digestive biscuits
- Marshmallows
- Chocolate

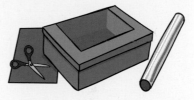

1 Prepare your shoe box. Carefully, cut a large hole in the lid. Using the glue stick, line the inside of the box with tin foil. Put the shiny side facing up so that it reflects the sun's heat. Place the open lid on top.

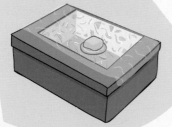

2 Place your oven in the sun to pre-heat. After 30 minutes put a biscuit in the bottom, with a marshmallow on top. Now cover the top of box with cling film.

3 Leave the oven in the sun until the marshmallow gets gooey and warm. Take it out and add a square of chocolate on top of the mushy marshmallow and top off with another biscuit. Press down gently to melt the chocolate. Yum!

DONE! DATE COMPLETED

27 MAKE AND FLY A QUICK KITE

There are many different types of kite, and here's a quick kite you can create from a simple brown bag!

YOU WILL NEED:

- Brown paper bag
- Markers, crayons, or whatever else to design and decorate your kite
- Hole punch
- Four pieces of string 50cm long
- Piece of string at least 2.5m long
- Sticky tape
- Several torn pieces of crêpe paper 20cm long

1 Get the bag ready. Decorate it with markers and doodle whatever you want!

hole punch

2 Open the paper bag and punch one hole at each of the four corners at the top of the bag. The hole should be about 2cm away from the rim.

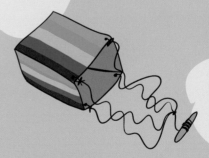

3 Push one 50cm piece of string through each of the holes and tie a knot so it stays in place. Once you have attached all four strings, tie their ends together and connect them to your 2.5m-long piece.

sticky tape

4 Tape a few pieces of crêpe paper to the closed end for your kite's tail.

5 Time for takeoff! Run fast and drag the kite behind you until it catches a gust of wind and flies into the air.

WHY NOT?
Experiment with kite materials. If you use a larger bag, will it fly faster? If you use a plastic bag, will it fly higher?

DONE!

DATE COMPLETED

28 LIGHT UP A LAVA LAMP

Those cool blobs you see in a lava lamp are simple to recreate. And you can make them glow, too!

YOU WILL NEED:

- Clean plastic bottle with cap (1.5l)
- Cooking oil
- Water
- Food colouring
- Indigestion tablet (broken into small bits) or rock salt
- Torch

1 Fill ¼ of the bottle with water and the remaining ¾ with oil. Add about 10 drops of food colouring.

2 Drop in the indigestion tablet, and screw on the cap. Now watch coloured bubbles rise as the tablets fizz!

3 Turn out the lights and shine a torch under the bottom of the bottle. YOU made that cool special effect. Way to go!

DONE!   DATE COMPLETED

CREATE A SUPER PSEUDONYM

Sometimes, famous authors write under a different name, called a 'pseudonym'. Inventing a made-up name can be loads of fun. Try it!

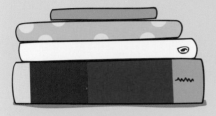

1 When selecting your pseudonym, you could mix and match some names from your favourite books or movies.

2 Or you could choose a name that's an anagram of your own. Like this!

MIKE FOSTER

MIKE FOSTER

TOM FERSKIE

3 Why not add a fancy title, like Sir or Queen? Theodor Seuss Geisel adopted a pseudonym to make his mother happy. She always hoped he'd be a doctor, so he called himself Dr Seuss!

WHY NOT?
Make up different names when writing a scary book, a joke book or a dramatic book.

4 Try coming up with a pseudonym signature in a different style. Practise signing your new name with swirls and zig-zags!

DONE!

DATE COMPLETED

30 REMEMBER ALMOST ANYTHING

Remembering things can be tricky, especially if you are studying for a super-important test! Here are some great tips to help.

I BEFORE E, EXCEPT AFTER C!

1 Take your time and concentrate when you study new material. Create a picture in your mind. Make visual associations to remember names and words. Make up a song or a rhyme with the details you need to recall.

2 Create a story timeline to remember an order of events or items. For example if you need to remember sunglasses and flipflops for a trip, you could say: "It was a bright and sunny morning when Mark bumped his toe..."

3 Use a 'mnemonic'. This memory trick works like a clever word puzzle. It's a sentence where the first letter of each word corresponds to another word. For example:

Naughty Elephant Shoots Water reminds us the directions on a compass in the order they appear, starting at the top: North, East, South and West.

DONE!   DATE COMPLETED

CREATE THREE COOL CODES

You've been chosen as a spy for a secret mission.
How do you plan to communicate?
In code, of course!

MAKE A CODE STICK

1 Take a pencil and wrap a long, thin piece of paper around it. Then write a message on the piece of paper. Once the message is written, remove the paper from the pencil. Your code will be tough to piece together to the untrained eye!

> THIS IS WHAT
> MIRROR WRITING
> LOOKS LIKE.
> NOW YOU TRY IT.

MESSAGE IN THE MIRROR

2 Take a sheet of paper and write a message while looking in a mirror. The letters should all be backwards. Without a mirror, the message looks like gobbledygook. With a mirror, the code message is instantly revealed.

CODE WORD: CHAPTERS

3 Many codes substitute letters for other ones. The one below uses the word CHAPTERS for the first eight letters of the alphabet, then lists the remaining letters of the alphabet in order. Swap the letters in your code from Row A to Row B!

C	H	A	P	T	E	R	S	B	D	F	G	I	J	K	L	M	N	O	Q	U	V	W	X	Y	Z	**Row A**
A	B	C	D	E	F	G	H	I	J	K	L	M	N	O	P	Q	R	S	T	U	V	W	X	Y	Z	**Row B**

Can you work out this message?
B GKVT QK NTCP!

DONE!   DATE COMPLETED

(Answer: I love to read!)

32 FOLD AND FLY A PERFECT PAPER PLANE

Ready for take-off? Grab a piece of paper and construct your own awesome aircraft to send soaring into the sky.

1 Fold the paper in half lengthways and open it up again.

2 Take the top right corner and fold it so it meets the centre crease. Do the same with the top left corner.

3 You should now have a triangle at the top of the paper.

4 Fold the triangle down towards the centre of the paper.

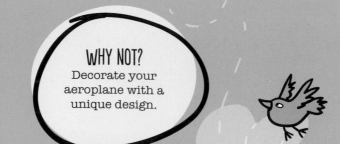

WHY NOT?
Decorate your
aeroplane with a
unique design.

5 Take the right corner and fold it in towards the centre. Do the same with the left corner. Make sure the two corner points touch.

6 Fold the paper in half along the crease you made in step 1.

7 To make the wings, fold the corners down towards the bottom of the aeroplane.

8 Grasp the plane from the bottom and launch it. Now watch it fly!

DONE!

DATE COMPLETED:

33 DEAL WITH AN EMERGENCY

Handling an emergency well starts with being prepared. Know where to seek help and to stay calm when you need to.

FIRST-AID KIT

Have a basic first-aid kit packed and ready at all times. You can buy a complete kit, but check that it contains these essential items.

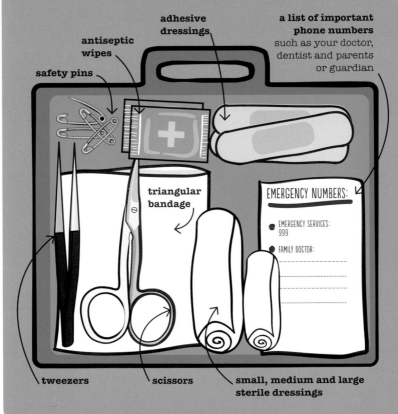

adhesive dressings

a list of important phone numbers such as your doctor, dentist and parents or guardian

antiseptic wipes

safety pins

triangular bandage

EMERGENCY NUMBERS:

- EMERGENCY SERVICES: 999
- FAMILY DOCTOR:

tweezers

scissors

small, medium and large sterile dressings

WRAP AN ARM SLING

Arm or wrist injuries can be very painful. Make your patient more comfortable by wrapping their injured arm in a supportive sling. If the injury is serious make sure they see a doctor or nurse as well.

1 Ask the person to sit down and support their injured arm, holding the wrist and hand slightly higher than the elbow.

2 Gently pull a triangle bandage between the arm and the chest so that one long end goes over the shoulder. Lift the lower part of the bandage over the arm and tie a knot beside the neck.

3 Bring the point of the sling by the elbow around the arm and secure it to the back of the bandage with a safety pin.

SAFTEY FIRST
If in doubt, call the emergency services. They will give you advice about what to do.

DONE!   DATE COMPLETED

34 GROW A WORM FARM

Make your own worm farm and watch these squirmy creatures dig, eat and make their way down into a new home!

YOU WILL NEED:
- Empty, 2-litre plastic bottle
- Scissors
- Small pebbles
- Sand
- Soil
- Black craft paper
- Sticky tape

1 Carefully cut the top off the bottle and tape the rim so there are no sharp edges. Also, poke a couple of small holes in the bottom for drainage. (Keep the cut off top – you will tape it back on top of the worm farm when you're done!)

2 Layer your materials. Put the pebbles at the bottom, then sand, soil, more sand and even more soil until you get to the top. You can use soil from your garden or a nearby park. Find worms in your garden or buy compost worms at a garden centre. Once the worm farm is ready, add the worms.

3 Wrap the black paper around the bottle to help recreate the worms' natural habitat, and glue the top back on with sticky tape. After a day, check to see how far your worms have tunnelled into their new home.

DONE!   DATE COMPLETED

BUILD A CITY OUT OF BOXES

Find everything it takes to make an entire city, using just the cardboard boxes you usually put in the recycling bin!

1 Get a bunch of boxes. You want different sizes and widths. Best bets: cereal boxes, shoe boxes, smaller snack boxes, juice boxes, cardboard tubes and spaghetti boxes (for skyscrapers, of course!). Wrap each box in paper.

2 Design and colour in your buildings using crayons, markers and paint. Draw windows, doors, bricks, tiles and whatever else you'd see on a building. How about plants, balconies or a teeny photo of you inside one of the windows?

3 Place your buildings in an area together to make a town. Once all the buildings are in place, you can add even more details such as streets or a park. This city is only limited by your imagination!

WHY NOT?
Make part of your town look like a famous building like the Empire State building, or the Gherkin!

DONE!   DATE COMPLETED

36 WEAVE YOUR WAY

Weaving has been around since the beginning of civilization. Make your own mini-loom – and learn to weave your own teeny tapestry.

YOU WILL NEED:

- Large piece of sturdy cardboard
- Scissors
- Tape
- Ruler to measure and pencil to mark measurements
- Strong string/wool – in different colours
- Needle with a wide hole

WHY NOT?

Use leftover wool to create a crazy colourful pattern!

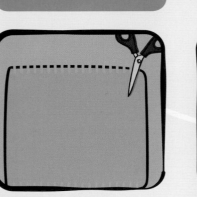

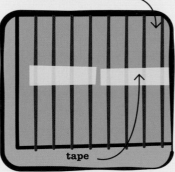

back of the loom

tape

1 Measure an even number of lines across the cardboard at about 1cm apart. At the top and bottom of the cardboard, cut little notches for the string to sit in as you wrap it around the loom.

2 Choose a specific colour for the threads stretched on the loom itself. Carefully wrap the thread around so it catches in the notches on either end. Then tape the threads down on the back side of your board, so they stay put while you weave.

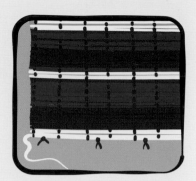

3 Choose another colour string and using a needle, carefully begin to weave it under and over each string in turn. When you reach the end of a row, start a second row above the first, starting above the last string you ended on.

4 Keep weaving until the entire loom has been filled. You can change to different colours of string along the way. Carefully push each row together keeping the rows straight. Remember not to pull the sides in too tight.

5 When you're done, turn over the loom and cut across the stuck-down threads. Now take one end off of the loom and tie the threads together in pairs to close the weaving. Your masterpiece is finished!

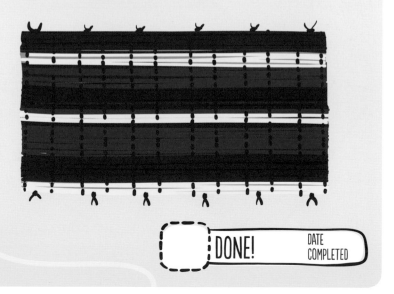

DONE!

DATE
COMPLETED

37 BE PREPARED FOR A NATURAL DISASTER

Hurricane! Earthquake! Flood! What would you do if you found yourself in the middle of a disaster? Here are a few survival tips.

SURVIVAL KIT

Be prepared before disaster strikes. Keep an emergency first-aid kit and a store of non-perishable food (like tins of beans) and bottles of water so you have them in case the power goes off. Don't forget to keep batteries, a torch and a blanket with your first-aid kit, too.

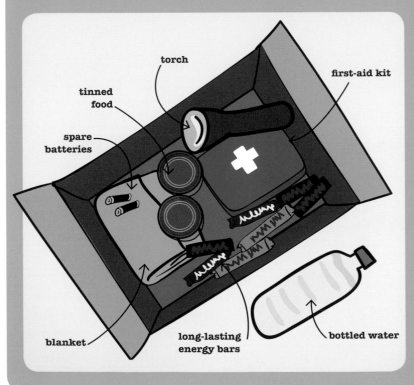

torch

tinned food

first-aid kit

spare batteries

blanket

long-lasting energy bars

bottled water

GET READY

Many things can happen during a natural disaster that are beyond your control. The best thing you can do is know how to react when the time comes! Here are some top tips for specific disasters.

HURRICANE

Fast winds may cause branches to break off the trees. Secure your windows and doors and move to a room inside your home as far away from windows as possible.

FLOOD

Heavy rains or storms can cause flooding in an area near water. Get as high up as possible in your home and listen to a local radio station for any evacuation orders.

EARTHQUAKE

An earthquake can loosen items inside in the home. Stay low, cover your head with your hands and crawl under a sturdy table.

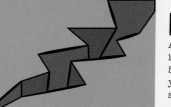

TORNADO

Fast winds can cause havoc in a small area. If indoors, stay on the lowest floor or basement. If outdoors, lie in a ditch.

DONE!   DATE COMPLETED

38 GET MAP SMART

Learn how to read three different types of map – without the need for a sat nav!

TYPES OF MAP

REGIONAL

Regional maps are the most common maps we use. They show us where places are and how to get from one place to another. You will find country borders, roads and railways as well as parks, lakes and rivers.

POLITICAL

Political maps are colour-coded to show different information such as population, languages or countries. There is a key to the map, called a legend, to explain what's being shown.

PHYSICAL

Physical maps show the way the land is shaped. Ragged, bumpy areas show where the land is mountainous or hilly. Green areas show where there are densely packed forests or jungles.

MAKE YOUR OWN MAP

Draw a map of your surrounding area using some pens, paper and a few cool symbols! Include important things that can help you find your way, such as buildings, roads, bus stops and green areas. Once you've finished colouring in your map you can add paths you use often, such as your way to school, a friend's house or to your local park.

MAP SYMBOLS

Here are some important symbols you'll find in many regional or city maps. Can you add some to your map?

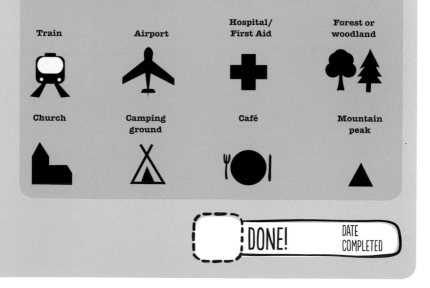

Train

Airport

Hospital/ First Aid

Forest or woodland

Church

Camping ground

Café

Mountain peak

DONE!

DATE COMPLETED

Locating and identifying animal tracks is so exciting. You just need to know what to look for – and where to look.

1 Look for prints on soft ground. This could be mud, sand or snow in the winter!

2 Tracks will be different depending on what the animal was doing. You can see whether it was walking or running, heavy or light, or even if it slipped!

3 Check out this chart to discover a few prints you may find in the wild, or even in your own back garden.

ANIMAL	TYPE OF PRINT
CAT	
DOG	
RABBIT	
SEAGULL	
SQUIRREL	

DONE! | DATE COMPLETED

USE CHOPSTICKS

Before eating, Japanese people say 'ita-daki-masu', which means, 'I receive this food'. Then they grab their chopsticks and eat! Can *you* do it?

1 Hold your hand out as if you are about to shake hands. Place the first chopstick between the crook of your thumb and the top of your ring finger.

2 Hold the second chopstick like a pencil with your thumb, index and middle finger. Important: the bottom chopstick does not move.

3 Use your thumb to hold the chopsticks firmly while you pivot the top chopstick to meet the bottom one. Use this motion to grasp the food!

GUESS WHAT?
In Japan it is considered rude to wave your chopsticks over your food. Go straight for the easiest piece!

DONE!   DATE COMPLETED

LEARN ABOUT YOUR STAR SIGN

The study of astrology believes we are born under one of twelve different zodiac signs. Does your star sign sound like you?

ARIES

The ram
(March 21st – April 19th)
Loyal, loves to be challenged
and works hard.

TAURUS

The bull
(April 20th – May 20th)
Glamorous, dependable, but
easily embarrassed!

GEMINI

The twins
(May 21st – June 20th)
Talkative, charming and caring.

CANCER

The crab
(June 21st – July 22nd)
Patient, protective and a little shy.

LEO

The lion
(July 23rd – August 22nd)
Playful, ambitious and loves being
the centre of attention.

VIRGO

The maiden
(August 23rd – September 22nd)
Dedicated, organised and
a perfectionist.

LIBRA

The scales
(September 23rd – October 22nd)
Great friend, artistic but a bit
rubbish at making decisions!

SCORPIO

The scorpion
(October 23rd – November 21st)
Intense, trusting and great
at keeping secrets!

SAGITTARIUS

The archer
(November 22nd – December 21st)
Gentle, good attitude but impatient!

CAPRICORN

The goat
(December 22nd – January 19th)
Realistic, generous and thoughtful.

AQUARIUS

The water-bearer
(January 20th – February 18th)
Peaceful, inventive and often quiet.

PISCES

The fish
(February 19th – March 20th)
Sympathetic, funny and emotional.

WHY NOT?
Look up your
daily horoscope in
a newspaper or
magazine!

DONE! DATE COMPLETED

42 DO PERFECT PUSH-UPS AND SIT-UPS

By doing these two simple exercises a few times each day, you give your body the tools it needs to stay strong.

PUSH-UP

1 Get into the plank position. This means just what it sounds like: you need to let your torso become as stiff as a board. Put your hands under your shoulders, with your torso and legs extended straight back. Be sure your back is straight.

WHY NOT?

You can kneel with your feet off the floor to make it easier.

2 Bend your arms to lower your body. Don't stick your bottom into the air or arch your back. You need to keep the strong 'plank' position as you lower your body. Then push yourself back up again!

SIT-UP

1 Lie on the floor with your back straight and your arms crossed over your chest. Bend your knees up, keeping your feet flat on the floor.

2 Slowly use your stomach muscles to raise your back off the floor into a sitting position. Then use your tummy muscles to guide you back to your first position again. Repeat!

Keep your feet on the floor!

SAFTEY FIRST!

Never strain yourself when you exercise, and stick to less than 10 repetitions a day.

DONE!

DATE COMPLETED

43 DREAM BIG

Scientists still don't fully understand why we dream, but the dreams that we do have, could have very specific meanings!

FALLING
You are feeling worried. Maybe it's about that big test coming up?

BEING CHASED
Someone is making you anxious.

INVISIBILITY
You need some love and attention.

FLYING
You are happy and feel free. Life is good!

TEETH
Lucky you! You might be rich one day.

MONSTERS
Something is making you feel afraid.

WHY NOT?
Keep a dream diary next to your bed. Record the details of your dream to analyse in the morning.

DONE!

DATE COMPLETED

PLAY THE INVINCIBLE BALLOON TRICK

Push a pin into a balloon and it goes pop, right?
Wow your friends with this simple trick!

1 Before you show the trick
to your audience, take your
balloon and stick a small strip
of clear sticky tape to it.

BANG!

2 Now for the trick! Hold
the balloon so that the
tape is facing away from
your audience. Say the magic
words while you take a pin
and carefully, (watch your
fingers!) push the pin into the
the balloon through the tape.
The balloon souldn't pop!

3 Lastly, to prove that the
balloon wasn't a fake, use
the pin to pop the balloon
and end your trick with a
bang!

DONE!   DATE COMPLETED

45 BE A REAL 'SEW' OFF

First, thread a needle – now, get useful! Sew a button and a patch. Whoa, you are 'sew' awesome!

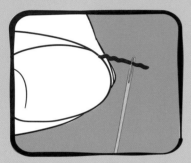

SEW ON A BUTTON

1 Cut 30cm of thread the same colour as the fabric you're sewing onto. Then thread the end through the 'eye' of your needle.

2 Take your button and place it where you want it to go. Poke the needle through the back of your fabric and one buttonhole, then down through the hole which is diagonal to it. Repeat this step with the other holes. Do this a total of at least six times, forming an 'X' across the button holes.

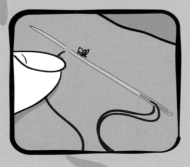

3 Once the button feels firm, sew a few small stitches in the back of the fabric, behind your button, to finish off. Watch where you're sticking the needle - you don't want to stick it into your finger!

PATCH UP JEANS

1 First, cut a square of fabric that is 4cm bigger than the hole around each side.

2 Carefully fold the edges of your patch inwards and pin in place on top of the hole.

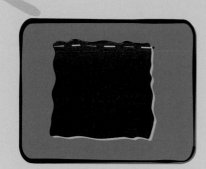

3 Sew small stitches about 0.5cm from the edge of your patch and the fabric to keep it secure. Be sure to watch your fingers!

WHY NOT?
Choose crazy fabric to make your jeans stand out from the crowd!

DONE!

DATE COMPLETED

46 MAKE YOUR OWN THAUMATROPE

Check out this cool trick, based on an invention called the thaumatrope. It plays a trick on your eyes to create one cool image!

1 Put two card circles on a table. Draw an empty fishbowl on one and a fish in the middle of the other. Colour both in.

2 Tape the two cards back to back with a pencil in the middle. Leave enough room at the bottom to place your palms over the pencil.

3 Place the pencil between your palms and spin it, quickly. The images on the cards should begin to blend together so you see the fish inside the fish tank!

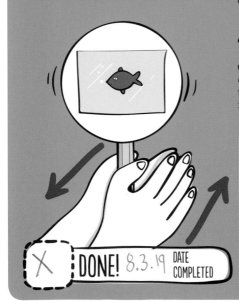

HOW IT WORKS:

The illusion works best when the pictures are continuously visible. If you spin very fast, your brain thinks the images are joined together. If you spin slowly, they just switch from one image to another.

X DONE! 8.3.19 DATE COMPLETED

BALANCE A SPOON
ON YOUR NOSE

At your next party, try this trick! Needed: a spoon and lot of concentration!

1 Grab a small spoon to perform your trick with. A teaspoon is perfect.

2 Rub the concave side of the spoon on your nose to get friction. Gently tilt your head back and keep rubbing. Once the spoon starts sticking to your nose let go of the handle!

3 Having trouble becoming 'attached' to your spoon? Breathe on it or rub it a few times with your index finger before trying again. That should help!

WHY NOT?
Do something else while you balance the spoon. Sing a few verses of a song, dance around or recite a poem.

DONE!   DATE COMPLETED

48 MAKE A FUNKY FLIPBOOK

Creating your own mini flipbook is like making a movie – only better, because you can make it with just paper, pencil and loads of imagination.

1 Get a stack of thin paper that's easy to flip. A pad of sticky notes or a small blank notebook would be perfect.

2 Choose your topic! You don't have to be a great artist – you can even draw walking stick figures or a bouncing ball. Keep it simple!

3 Start at the last sheet of your pad and draw your first image. Go to the next page and trace it, changing it slightly as you go along to create the movement.

4 Bigger changes from one drawing to the next will appear as faster motion when you flip. Smaller changes will seem slower.

5 Add a background, like rolling clouds and a sun, that changes position with each frame, so it all appears to be moving.

6 Once you're satisfied with your flipbook, outline the drawings in pen to make them easier to see. Now, start from the bottom page and flip the pages to watch your masterpiece come to life!

WHY NOT?
Add special effects! Put words flashing in the background or a bird flying towards you!

DONE!

DATE
COMPLETED

49 MAKE A SOCK PUPPET WITH ATTITUDE

You can make an effortlessly cool puppet from the simplest of items: a sock!

YOU WILL NEED:
- Large sock
- Piece of thick cardboard
- Scissors
- Wool (optional)
- Two buttons, googly eyes, pipe cleaners and other craft bits you can find
- Fabric glue

1 Cut a large oval from the cardboard and fold it in half. This will be your puppet's mouth.

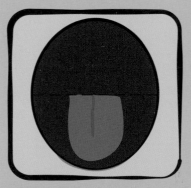

2 Decorate the oval so it looks like a mouth. You could add a tongue, teeth or even words!

3 Stick your hand inside the sock and find the 'mouth'. Put your thumb in the heel of the sock and your other fingers in the toes.

4 Dot some fabric glue inside the crease and insert the cardboard mouth. Leave to dry.

5 Finally, decorate your puppet with whatever other materials you want to make it more like an original character: a fake wig (with wool), funny ears (with pipe cleaners), or perhaps a swatch of fabric for a cape!

wool hair

button eyes

felt tongue

WHY NOT?
Once you've made your sock puppet, give it a personality. Turn the page and learn to let it talk for itself!

DONE! 8.3.18 DATE COMPLETED

50 BE A VENTRILOQUIST

Now you've created your puppet, it's time to make it talk!

BLAH BLAH BLAH BLAH

1 Capture your audience's attention by saying something as simple as, "Did you hear that?" The question will make them listen more closely.

2 'Swallow' your actual voice and speak, moving your mouth as little as possible. You want to control your breathing and talk from 'inside' your mouth.

3 Saying the letters B, F, M, P, Q, V and W is very challenging. Try using the substitutions in this chart:

DONE!   DATE COMPLETED

SOUND	TIP
For B	replace it with a 'geh' sound at the back of the throat
For F	use a 'th' sound so 'fabulous' becomes 'thabulous'
For M	use 'nah' or 'neh' instead so 'master' becomes 'nah-ster'
For P	use 'kl' in the back of your throat, so 'paint' becomes 'klaint'
For Q	stretch out the sound so it's 'koo'
For V	just like F, use the 'th' sound
For W	use 'oooh' at the start of a word so 'welcome' would sound like 'oooh-elcome'

SHAKE SOME ICE CREAM

You can make real ice cream with nothing more than a plastic bag and a few other simple items!

YOU WILL NEED:

- 1 small-size zip-locked bag
- 1 large-size zip-locked bag
- Lots of ice cubes (to fill a large plastic bag)
- 230ml cream
- 60g rock salt
- 2 tablespoons sugar
- 1/2 teaspoon vanilla extract
- Yummy items to flavour the ice cream, like chocolate chips, nuts or fresh fruit

1 Combine sugar, cream and vanilla in a bowl and pour into the small bag. Seal tightly.

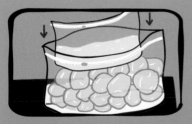

2 Place the salt and ice in the large bag. Then put the sealed smaller bag inside the large bag.

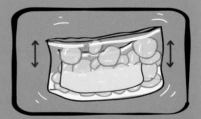

3 Seal the larger bag. Shake until the mixture hardens. It should take about 5-10 minutes. Ta-da! You've got ice cream!

WHY NOT?

Add toppings to your ice cream once it's frozen. You could use fresh fruit or chocolate sauce!

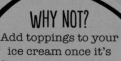

cherry

chocolate sauce

DONE!   DATE COMPLETED

HAVE FUN WITH PEN AND PAPER

Get set for gaming fun! All you need is a pen, some paper and a friend or two!

HANGMAN

Think of a word and give your friend the subject (such as a place, person, sport, film or TV show). For example, we've used *Italy* below. Next, draw a line for each letter in your word. Your friend then chooses letters they think could be in the word, one at a time. If a letter is correct, write it on your lines in its position. However, if it's wrong, add a line to your hangman! Your friend has six tries to guess the word before the hangman drawing is complete. These are the steps to complete your drawing:

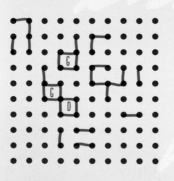

SQUARES

First, draw a grid of dots, around 10x10 (like you can see on the left). Now, take it in turns to draw lines between the dots. The aim is to complete a square on your turn. When you complete a square, write your initial inside, or colour it in. The person with the most squares when all the lines are filled in is the winner!

CHARADES

You'll need at least three of you to play this one. First, cut or rip paper into little slips. Write names of books, TV shows and films on separate slips of paper. Now fold them and mix them up in a pile. Take it in turns to pick out a slip of paper, then 'act' out silent clues to get your friends to guess what it is. There's only one rule – you can't make a sound! Here are ways to show what you're acting out:

BOOK

FILM

TV SHOW

YOU GOT IT!

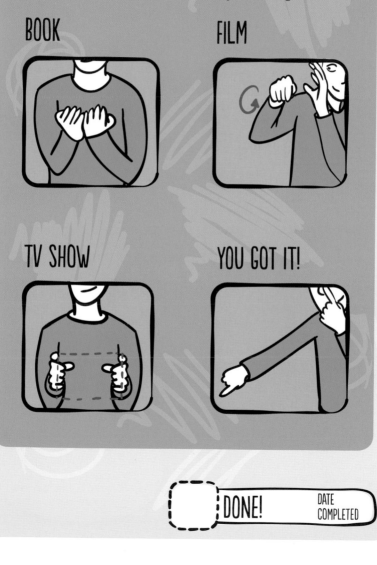

DONE!

DATE
COMPLETED

53 INVENT A BOARD GAME

The next time it's a rainy day, don't just play any old game – design your own!

1 First up, design your board. The simplest board shape is square with 10 smaller squares on each side. Choose some of the squares to be 'active' squares and colour them in.

2 Choose what kind of game you'd like to make. Do you like answering questions or doing dares? Come up with fun things to do each time you or your friends land on one of your active squares. Write them on small cards or bits of paper and place them face down in the middle.

3 Before you start playing, come up with some fun rules to stick by. Roll a dice and take it in turns to move around the board.

TELL A JOKE!

DON'T FORGET!
You need game pieces to move around the board! You could use beads, coins, figures or sweets.

DONE!   DATE COMPLETED

DO A SKATEBOARD TRICK

One of the key tricks in skateboarding is a jump called the Ollie. Remember to **always** wear a helmet when using your skateboard!

SKATEBOARD PARTS:

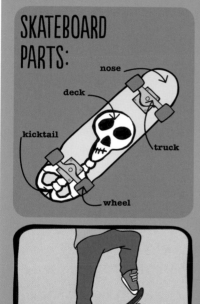

nose
deck
kicktail
truck
wheel

1 Bend your knees. As you roll (slowly!), slam your right foot down as hard as you can on the kicktail and then jump into the air (above skateboard) with both feet.

2 As you go up into the air, drag your left foot up the deck. It will take time and practice to get the feel for this, so keep trying.

3 Bend your knees as you come down to soften the impact. Soon you will be doing an Ollie everywhere you skate!

DONE! DATE COMPLETED

55 LEARN THE SEVEN WONDERS OF THE WORLD

The most famous list of wonders counts seven from ancient times. Some landmarks remain, while others have disappeared over time.

1. THE GREAT PYRAMIDS OF GIZA

When? 2,500 BCE

What? Stone tombs built 250m wide and 125m high, with more than 2 million blocks of stone.

Cool fact: Each stone block weighs more than a car!

2. THE HANGING GARDENS OF BABYLO

When? Unknown

What? Lush gardens with tree roots that grew into doorways and roads.

Cool fact: There is no formal record of the garden, leading many to believe it was made up

3. THE TEMPLE OF ARTEMIS AT EPHESUS

When? 6th century BCE

What? Awesome towering temple built in honour of Artemis, the Greek goddess of hunting.

Cool fact: The temple was destroyed by floods, earthquakes and raids.

4. THE COLOSSUS OF RHODES

When? 292 BCE

What? Enormous 30m statue of Helios, the patron god of Rhodes.

Cool fact: After a battle, leftover armour was melted down to make this statue.

5. THE LIGHTHOUSE OF ALEXANDRIA

When? 3rd century BCE

What? The world's first lighthouse tower used to guide sailors at sea.

Cool fact: It used mirrors to reflect sunlight during the day. At night, men burned fires to create a guiding light.

6. THE STATUE OF ZEUS AT OLYMPIA

When? 5th century BCE

What? Enormous throned figure of Zeus made from ivory, gold, wood and other materials.

Cool fact: The statue held a small sculpture of Nike, the goddess of victory, in his right hand.

7. THE MAUSOLEUM AT HALICARNASSUS, TURKEY

When? 4th century BCE

What? Decorated with columns and sculpted carvings.

Cool fact: Built for King Mausolus. The word 'mausoleum,' which means above-ground tomb, comes from his name.

DONE!

DATE COMPLETED

56 BE A MAD SCIENTIST

By mixing together ordinary items from the kitchen, you can change the colour of liquids in a flash!

YOU WILL NEED:

- mixing bowl, ideally glass
- 7 clear plastic drinking cups
- Red cabbage
- Kitchen knife
- Approximately 120ml of the following 7 liquids:
  - Lemon juice
  - Vinegar
  - Bicarbonate of soda
  - Clear or coloured washing-up liquid
  - Ketchup
  - Lemonade or cola
  - Tap water

1 Carefully chop the cabbage and put small pieces into a bowl with 250ml of water, then mash it with a fork until the water turns bright purple. Pour 20-30ml of the liquid into each of the plastic cups.

2 Now add 20-30mls of your 7 liquids to the cups individually, making a note of which liquid has been added where. The liquids in the cups should change colour!

THE RESULTS

When the cabbage juice turns red, it means that your other liquid is **acidic**, like the lemon. When the juice goes blue, it means the substance is **alkaline**, like the baking soda. If the colour doesn't change it means your mixer is **neutral**.

DONE! DATE COMPLETED

Going camping needs lots of planning and organisation – get clued up by reading this page!

tent

camping chair

map of the area

torch

ground mat

first-aid kit

food

BE PREPARED

Pack essential items you need for a good night's sleep in the wild, such as a tent, a sleeping bag and a ground mat. Think about where you are planning to camp and what the weather is like, and take the right clothing to keep you warm. Also, remember a first-aid kit, food, a torch and a map for the ultimate (and safe) outdoor experience!

SAFETY FIRST

Make sure that you tell someone where you are at all times, and never camp alone!

DONE!

DATE COMPLETED

58 BE A KNOW IT ALL

Impress your friends with your amazing knowledge. Here are some too-cool facts to share!

Like fingerprints, everyone's **tongue** print is different.

Only 20% of the Earth's deserts are covered in sand, while others are covered in **snow**.

Your **arm span** is the same length as your **height**. True story!

Frogs never close their eyes, even when they **sleep**.

It would take 1.2 million mosquitoes, all of them biting at once, to **completely drain** a human body of all its **blood**.

Most of the dust in your house is actually **dead skin cells**.

Cats sleep about **16 to 18 hours** each day.

WHY NOT?
Write down any new facts you find in your journal? Take a look at activity 60 to make your own!

DONE!

DATE COMPLETED

The clouds above your head aren't just there to look pretty, they can tell you LOADS about the weather!

CIRRUS

Cirrus clouds are the thin wispy clouds often seen against a clear sky, formed by ice crystals. It should stay nice and dry for the time being!

ALTOCUMULUS

These clouds look like little clumps. Lots put together will create storm clouds.

CUMULUS

These are the big fluffy clouds that look like cotton wool and disappear before the sun goes down. Lots of them can mean showers later on!

CUMULONIMBUS

When it's grey outside, it's probably because a cumulonimbus cloud is covering the sky! It means that it's raining where you are, or nearby.

DONE!

DATE COMPLETED

60 MAKE YOUR OWN JOURNAL

Writing a journal is really fun, and could even help you become a great writer! Follow these simple tips to make your very own journal.

YOU WILL NEED:

- A3 Card
- Lined A4 paper
- Crayons, stickers and markers for decoration
- Stapler
- Ribbon

1 Take a piece of A3 card and fold in half (like a birthday card) – this will be the cover for your journal, so decorate it however you like!

2 Now use a hole punch to punch two holes half-way down your cover, close to the fold.

3 Take sheets of lined A4 paper and use your hole-punch to make holes halfway down the paper on the left hand side. These will make up the inside pages of your journal.

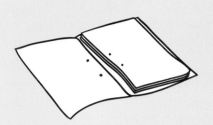

4 Place your A4 sheets inside your cover, and make sure that all the holes match up.

5 Thread a length of ribbon through the holes in your cover and inside pages, then tie in a bow.

6 Your journal is ready to use! You could also make one with plain paper to use as a sketch book.

MY JOURNAL

WHY NOT?
Create a code that only you can understand to keep snooping eyes away from your journal!

DONE!

DATE COMPLETED

61 LEARN THE PHASES OF THE MOON

As the moon travels around the earth it seems to change shape. These shapes are called phases. What phase is the moon in tonight?

First quarter

Waxing gibbous

Waxing cresent

Full Moon

SHAPE SHIFTER

The moon looks like it's changing shape because the light from the Sun hits it at different angles as it travels around the earth. It takes 29.5 days for the moon to travel once around the Earth.

New Moon

Waning gibbous

Waning crescent

Last quarter

DONE! | DATE COMPLETED

63 MAKE A KITCHEN VOLCANO

Make your very own volcano with just a few items from your kitchen cabinet. Be sure to ask your parents, first!

YOU WILL NEED:

- Modelling clay
- 1 litre plastic bottle with lid
- Red food colouring
- Washing up liquid
- White vinegar
- 30g baking powder
- Warm water
- Plastic funnel
- Baking tray

1 On the baking tray, shape your clay around the plastic bottle to create a mountain shape. Leave the top of the bottle open and make sure nothing drops inside.

2 Mix a few drops of food colouring with water until it turns a fiery shade of red.

3 Pour the red water into your 'mountain' opening using the funnel.

DID YOU KNOW?

• The word 'volcano' comes from the Roman god of fire, Vulcan.

• The largest known volcano in the universe is Olympus Mons, a volcano on the planet Mars. It measures 372 miles wide, which is as big as the entire country of Austria!

• One of Jupiter's moons is completely covered in volcanoes.

4 Carefully add six drops of the washing up liquid and 30 grams of baking powder into the mountain, too.

5 Now it's time for your volcano to erupt! Slowly pour your white vinegar through the funnel – you won't need much before the eruption begins!

WHY NOT?
Cover your baking tray with sand and add some toy dinosaurs for a prehistoric volcano scene!

DONE! DATE COMPLETED

64 3 WAYS TO TRICK YOUR BRIAN

These simple optical illusions seem straight forward but some things are not always as they seem at first glance!

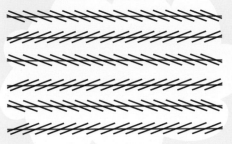

1 The red lines look like they're tilted, but are they?

In fact they're perfectly straight! The illusion was discovered by German astrophysicist Johann Karl Friedric Zöllner.

2 Which one of the red circles below is the biggest?

Think you've got it? Well actually they're both the same size, it's just that the small circles surrounding the one at the bottom make it look bigger.

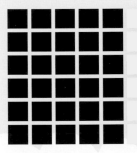

3 The grid above is made of squares, but can you see spots?

This illusion is called a scintillating grid.

DONE!   DATE COMPLETED

MAKE A SNOW GLOBE

Snow globes show a miniature scene with 'snow' falling around it. Have a go at making your own!

1 Take a small jar with a lid (a jam jar is perfect). Clean out the inside and remove all labels.

2 On the inside of the lid, glue down small objects like figurines or old board game pieces. Use strong glue so that nothing will come loose inside the jar.

3 Fill the jar with water almost to the top and add a drop or two of glycerine (you can find this in the baking aisle at the supermarket). Now pour in a spoonful of glitter.

4 Carefully put the lid back on the filled jar and screw it shut tight. Then flip over and shake!

DONE!   DATE COMPLETED

66 MAKE A SHORT FILM

Making a film with friends can be a lot of fun!
Follow the tips below, and create your own
masterpiece. Start with the four S's.

SCRIPT

1 Once you've got an idea of your
story and characters, you can
write a script for each of your
actors to learn.

STORYBOARD

2 Make up a storyboard (a rough,
comic-strip style, version of your
story) to use as a guide along
the way. Draw a quick sketch of how
you want each shot to look.

SPECIAL EFFECTS

3 Make-up, wigs and other
costume elements can turn a
friend into a superstar actor!

SET AND SCENERY

4 You don't need to go to any
special locations to get great
shots. Your own house is an
excellent place to start. See if you
can get your family and friends to
be in your cast!

THE WIDE SHOT

Use this shot to show where the action is taking place, and to set the scene.

OVER THE SHOULDER

This shot shows the action from your character's point of view.

CLOSE UP

Use this shot to clearly show your character's emotions and their reactions.

EXTREME CLOSE UP

This shot is great for focusing attention on small details. Using an extreme close up of a character's face is a great way of creating a sense of tension.

DONE!   DATE COMPLETED

67 BUNNYHOP ON A BMX

Impress your friends by mastering this awesome trick! Remember to **always** wear a helmet, in case you fall off.

1 Start by pushing forward slowly. Get ready to pull the front of the bike up.

2 Pull the front wheel up. As it starts to move back towards the ground, use your legs to kick the back of the bike up.

WHY NOT?
Get a friend to film
your new BMX skills.
For ideas on making a
short film see activity
66!

3 With both of the wheels off the
ground, you can hop over your
obstacle!

4 For a smooth landing, bend
your arms and knees as you
land back on the ground. You
should always try to land on the
back wheel, or both wheels.

DONE!

DATE
COMPLETED

68 WRITE WITH INVISIBLE INK

Want to send a secret message to your friend? Here's one sure-fire way to get the word out - without anyone seeing a thing!

YOU WILL NEED:
- Paintbrush or cotton bud
- White paper
- Lemon juice
- Small bowl
- Lamp

1 Dip your paintbrush or cotton bud lightly in the lemon juice and write a message on white paper. Don't use too much, you want it to dry quickly.

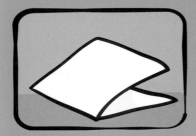

2 As the paper dries, the message will disappear. Fold it up and give it to your friend.

3 To read the note, hold the paper close to a lamp. When the paper warms up, the lemon juice will magically reveal your message!

DONE!   DATE COMPLETED

HOW TO READ YOUR OWN PALM

For centuries, people have been telling the future by reading palms. Take a look at your own hand to see what's in store for *you*.

Girdle of Venus
Not everyone has one of these, but if you do, it means you are a sensitive soul!

Heart line
Reveals your emotional side. If you have a wavy line, it means you are very caring.

Sun line
If you have a strong sun line, it could mean that you'll be famous one day!

Head line
Shows how you think about things. If it's long, you're probably very intelligent. If it's curved, you're creative!

Life line
This shows your inner strength. The deeper it is, the tougher you are.

DONE!

DATE COMPLETED

70 CREATE YOUR OWN OBSTACLE COURSE

One of the best rainy day activities is a homemade obstacle course! Use objects from around your home to make yours.

START

1 Toy Toss: Put a laundry basket at one end of the room, grab an armful of cuddly toys and cushions, and try to throw them in. Get three out of five in the basket before moving on to the next stage!

2 Funny jumps: At this stop on the course, each player does a sequence of jumps in the air. Do a star jump, a frog jump and a bunny hop.

3 Hula-paloola: Place a hula hoop on the floor and jump in and out of it ten times with your feet together.

4 Tunnel time: Make a tunnel using a big sheet or quilt and some chairs. Climb through the tunnel and then back again before racing to the next stage!

5 Tightrope walk: Place a scarf in a straight line along the floor and pretend you are a circus performer! Walk across the scarf without stepping over the edges, and hold your arms out to the side to help you balance.

6 Hat's the way to do it! Get a pile of hats, scarves and gloves. Each player must put them all on, strike a pose, then take them all off again!

FINISH

DONE!

DATE COMPLETED

71 PAINT LIKE A FAMOUS ARTIST

You can create art in the style of some of the world's greatest artists! Here are two famous artist's techniques to inspire you.

SPLATTER PAINTING

The American artist Jackson Pollock used this technique to create some of his most famous works. Why not have a go yourself?

YOU WILL NEED:
- Paper and card
- Paints
- Paintbrushes
- Newspaper
- Sticky tape
- Pencil
- PVA glue

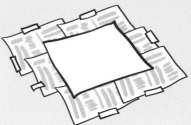

1 First, tape your newspaper onto the floor. This will keep the floor from getting too messy. Put your blank canvas or paper on top of the newspapers.

2 Stand over the canvas and dip your paintbrush in the paint, then shake and splatter colour from left to right. Do this several times with different colours.

IMPASTO PAINTING

Impasto is a way of painting where the paint is layered on very thickly so the brush marks can still be seen. The Dutch artist Vincent Van Gogh often used this technique.

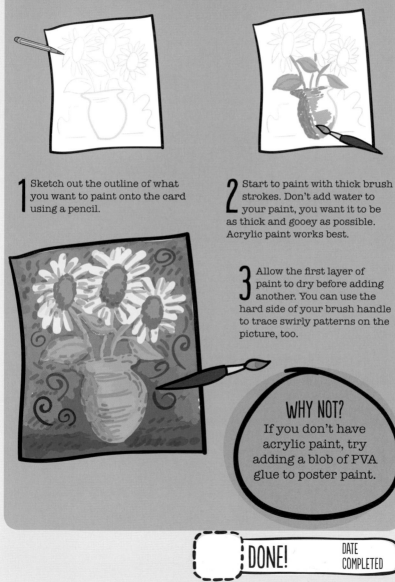

1 Sketch out the outline of what you want to paint onto the card using a pencil.

2 Start to paint with thick brush strokes. Don't add water to your paint, you want it to be as thick and gooey as possible. Acrylic paint works best.

3 Allow the first layer of paint to dry before adding another. You can use the hard side of your brush handle to trace swirly patterns on the picture, too.

WHY NOT?
If you don't have acrylic paint, try adding a blob of PVA glue to poster paint.

DONE!

DATE COMPLETED

72 MAKE A FUNKY CRESS HEAD

These cool cress heads have hair you can eat!
Why not make a whole gang?

1 Take a clean yogurt pot and use felt-tips or paint to draw a funny face.

2 Next, half fill the pot with damp cotton wool.

3 Sprinkle some cress seeds onto the cotton wool and press them down gently. Leave your cress head on a sunny windowsill but make sure the cotton wool doesn't dry out.

4 When the cress has fully grown you can snip it off to use in a sandwich or salad. Yum!

DONE! DATE COMPLETED

THROW A SUPER SLEEPOVER

Hosting a sleepover is so much fun!
Check out our top tips for an awesome night.

THE INVITE

Make your invitation! These can be on paper, by
email or text message. Choose a party theme such
as sports, music or movie marathon.

FOOD

Stock up on your favourite snacks! Popcorn,
crisps, and vegetable sticks with dips are great.

STUFF TO DO

Make a list of games and activities that you and your
friends like, so you aren't ever stuck for something to
do. Why not have each of your guests bring a favorite
movie or game so that you have a big selection to
choose from? You can also make up ghost
stories after lights out!

SLEEP (NOT!)

Find the best place for everyone to
get into their sleeping bags. Gather
up loads of squashy pillows and
blankets and get comfortable!

WHY NOT?

Use some other
activities in this
book to keep you and
friends entertained!

DONE!

DATE
COMPLETED

74 PLAY TRAVEL GAMES

Do you get bored on long trips? Next time you're on a long journey, why not have a go at these fun games? You'll be there before you know it!

EAT THE ALPHABET

Come up with funny things to eat for each letter of the alphabet. Announce, 'I'm so hungry, I could eat an alligator'. The next player continues with a B word. They might say, 'I'm so hungry, I could eat an alligator and a beach ball!' Keep it going until everyone in the car is eating zips!

THE PLACE NAME GAME

The first person thinks of the name of a place (town, city or country anywhere in the world), for example 'London'. Then, the next person has to try and think of a place name beginning with the last letter of that place name, for example 'Nepal'. See how long you can keep it going!

GUESS THE THEME TUNE

Each player takes turns to hum (no singing the words!) a TV theme tune. The first person to guess the tune gets to go next.

NEW YORK

KENYA

DONE! DATE COMPLETED

MAKE THE BEST HOT CHOCOLATE

If you've only ever tried powdered hot chocolate, then you're in for a real treat!

1 Ask an adult to heat up some milk. Meanwhile, break up a small bar of dark chocolate into a heatproof jug.

2 Carefully, pour a third of the hot milk over the chocolate, and whisk. Leave to stand for a minute.

3 Add in the rest of the milk, whisking all the time, untill the milk and chocolate are completly combined. Enjoy in your favorite mug!

WHY NOT?
Sprinkle some mini marshmallows on top of your hot chocolate for an extra treat!

DONE!   DATE COMPLETED

76 GO ON A SCAVENGER HUNT

Go searching for items and collect everything on your list before your friends do!

WHERE TO PLAY

Your back garden or a local park would be perfect places to hold a scavenger hunt, but they work indoors too. Once you've chosen a place to play, make sure all of your players know where they should be looking, and not to go outside that area. Always make sure that an adult knows where you are if your hunt is outside of your home.

MAKE A LIST

Start by coming up with a list of things for your player to find. Here are some suggestions:

ON AN OUTDOOR HUNT:

- Pinecone
- Flower
- Leaf larger than your hand
- Leaf smaller than your palm
- Something that smells nice
- Something round
- Feather
- Piece of bark
- Twig shaped like a "Y"

ON AN INDOOR HUNT:

- Toothbrush
- Book
- DVD
- Cushion
- Pillow
- Spoon
- Odd sock
- Rubber duck
- A clothes peg

SECRET ITEMS!

Hide some funny items (like an egg cup or a rubber duck) around the search area. Tell your players that whoever finds these bonus items gets a special prize! If you want to join in the hunt, ask an adult to do this for you.

THE WINNER IS...

The first person to collect all the items on their list is the winner! When everyone comes back, take a good look at your collection.

WHY NOT?

Give extra prizes for the biggest leaf, the most unusual item and the nicest flower.

DONE!

DATE COMPLETED

77 MAKE YOUR OWN NEWSPAPER

Making your own newspaper is a fun way to sharpen your writing skills and get your imagination going!

THE FRONT PAGE

Each **front page** shows one or two **headlines**. Words in headlines are large and need to catch the reader's attention.

THE
WEEKLY WOOF

Date: Weather: Price:

DOG FINDS LOST BONE AFTER 2 YEARS
It was in the back garden all along!

Masthead

Name your newspaper and create a **masthead**. This will be the most-noticeable part of your front page. Add on all the details you would find on real paper: date, weather forecast and price.

Headline

Photo

INSIDE YOUR NEWSPAPER

When you have made your **front page**, you can make the rest of
your paper. Fill out the pages with smaller headlines, more articles
and more stories. When it's finished, staple it together – and it's
ready for the newsstand!

Write your **article**. Your story can be about
anything you like! It could be a made up event,
or something that's really happened to you or
your family.

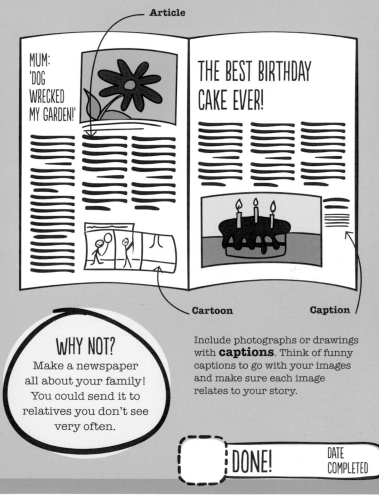

Article

MUM: 'DOG WRECKED MY GARDEN!'

THE BEST BIRTHDAY CAKE EVER!

Cartoon

Caption

WHY NOT?
Make a newspaper
all about your family!
You could send it to
relatives you don't see
very often.

Include photographs or drawings
with **captions**. Think of funny
captions to go with your images
and make sure each image
relates to your story.

DONE!

DATE COMPLETED

MAKE A TIE-DYE T-SHIRT

Be creative and turn a plain white t-shirt into a cool new top!

YOU WILL NEED:

- White T-shirt
- Disposable tablecloth or rubbish bags
- Fabric dyes in your favourite colours
- Rubber bands
- Small bowl
- Large bowl
- Rubber gloves
- Salt
- Plastic squeeze bottles
- Plastic bag

1 Cover your work surface with the tablecloth or rubbish bags. Roll the T-shirt up from the collar to the bottom and tie rubber bands around it.

2 Wearing rubber gloves, carefully mix up the fabric dye with water in a jug (following the instructions on the packet), and pour the mixture into your squeezy bottle. You can do this with as many colours as you like!

3 Put warm salt water into a bowl and dip the shirt into the water. Take it out after a minute or two.

4 On your protected work surface, squeeze your fabric dye on to each section of the rubber-band tied T-shirt.

5 When you have applied the colour, put the dyed T-shirt into a plastic bag and leave it overnight. The next day, run your T-shirt under cold water while wearing your rubber gloves to protect your hands. Rinse the shirt until the water runs clear. Then remove the rubber bands!

6 Ask a grown-up to place the T-shirt into the washer (on its own!) and run it through a cold water cycle. Then let it air dry. For the next few washes, always wash this t-shirt separately.

WHY NOT?
Try different colours and ways of tying your T-shirt to get different effects.

DONE!

DATE COMPLETED

79 MAKE BALLOON SWAN

Turn a balloon into a beautiful swan and impress your party guests!

Twist here

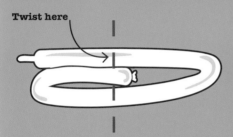

1 Use a long, thin balloon for this trick. Inflate your balloon most of the way, leaving 5-10cm at the end. Bend the whole balloon into a large circle so that the knot is halfway inside the circle. Grab the balloon at the centre and twist all the way around, holding the knot.

2 This will make two loops, and the part with the uninflated end should be poking up. This will be the swan's head. Fold the left hand loop of the balloon back through the right hand loop to make a 'balloon body'.

Squeeze here

3 While holding the top end, squeeze the air from the inflated part around the bend in the balloon. This makes the balloon stay in a bent position that's just right for the swan's head!

DONE!   DATE COMPLETED

PLAY A TRICK ON YOURSELF

Can you trick your own body? Why not test yourself with these amazing tricks.

APPLES AND ORANGES

Take an apple and an orange, and while taking a bite of the apple, hold the orange under your nose. Does the apple taste different? Your sense of smell and taste are very closely linked, so you might find that the apple starts to taste like an orange!

THE TAP TEST

Place your hand palm down on a flat surface, like a table top. Without moving your other fingers try tapping your third finger. Easy, right? Now tuck your middle finger under your palm and try again. You should find it impossible to move! This is because your second and third fingers share a tendon.

WHY NOT?
Put on a magic show for your family and friends. See page 16 for more ideas.

DONE!

DATE COMPLETED

81 MAKE A CHEWING GUM WRAPPER BRACELET

This bracelet is not only fun to make - you'll be recycling when you make it! You can make this bracelet from any sweet wrapper or scrap paper, but chewing gum wrappers are perfect.

1 Fold one long side in towards the middle of the wrapper, then do the same with the other side. Next, fold the whole thing in half lengthwise, to form a thin strip.

2 Bend your wrapper in the middle, then fold in each long end in to meet the middle.

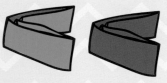

3 Repeat steps 1-2 with your next bit of wrapper. Using different colours will create a pattern.

4 Insert the flat ends of one folded wrapper into the side openings of the next, so that they slot into each other and make a 'v' shape.

5 Repeat the first four steps with your folded wrappers to form a zigzag chain.

6 When your bracelet is long enough to fit around your wrist, make one more link, but don't fold the last two folds.

7 Insert these sides into the openings of your first wrapper, and close the bracelet by folding the long strips in. After a bit of practice your bracelet should look like this!

WHY NOT?
Try different colour combinations and make bracelets for all of your friends!

DONE!   DATE COMPLETED

WALK THROUGH PAPER

Amaze your friends by walking through a single sheet of paper!

THE PERFORMANCE

1 Ask the audience if they think that you can cut a hole in an A4 piece of paper large enough to walk

2 Cut along the lines carefully in front of the audience. Tell some jokes to keep them entertained!

3 Stretch the paper apart carefully and walk through it. Ta-da!

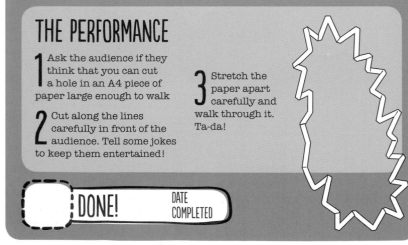

DONE!   DATE COMPLETED

MAKE PAPER CUP SPEAKERS

Make your own handy pair of paper cup speakers for your phone or MP3 player!

YOU WILL NEED:

- A pair of earbud heaphones
- Four paper drinking cups
- Two toothpicks
- Sellotape
- Small scissors

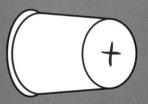

1 Use the toothpicks to carefully make a small, cross-shaped slit in the base of the two cups that will be the speakers.

2 Insert the ear buds all the way through the holes, until only the wire is left outside the cup.

3 Turn the remaining cups upside down, then place your 'speakers' sideways on top. Selloape the sides to secure them into place. Plug the ear buds into an MP3 player and play some tunes!

DONE!

DATE COMPLETED

84 BLOW GIANT BUBBLES

Make your own oversized wand to blow gigantic bubbles!

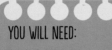

1 Measure out 2m of string and thread through both straws. Tie the ends of your string together, then space out your straws to make the handles of your bubble wand.

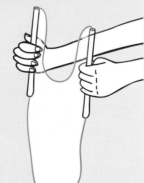

2 Put all of the ingredients for your bubble mixture into a washing up bowl, and mix them together.

3 Dip your bubble wand into the mixture. Raise it up into the air, and slowly walk backwards. Don't be put off if it doesn't work the first time – you'll soon be making mind-blowing bubbles!

DONE! DATE COMPLETED

MAKE GLOW-IN-THE-DARK GOO

85

Make a batch of crazy, glow-in-the-dark gloop!

YOU WILL NEED:

- 350ml of water
- Glow-in-the-dark paint (you can get this from craft or stationery shops)
- 260g Cornflour
- Bowl
- Wooden spoon
- Measuring cups

1 Mix the cornflour with water, a little at a time. Stir until the mixture becomes dough-like.

2 Add the glow in the dark paint. Mix again until it's completely mixed together.

3 Once your slime is ready to handle, hold it close to a light to activate the glow in the dark magic.

TOP TIP

Don't forget to wash your hands when you are finished, and store any leftover slime in a sealed sandwich bag.

DONE!

DATE COMPLETED

86 GO ON A GHOSTHUNT

Want a scary adventure? Grab some friends and search for ghosts! Here's how to track down spirits lurking in your neighbourhood...

GET READY

Once you are in the room, or space that you're ghost-hunting in, be as calm and peaceful as possible. Turn out the lights, or dim them if you're feeling a bit wobbly! Take notes of everything you see, hear and feel.

ASK QUESTIONS

Once the room or space is as quiet as possible, ask the ghosts questions, such as "Is anyone there?" or "Can you give us a sign?". See what happens after you've asked your question.

IS ANYBODY THERE?

UH-OH!

Once you've heard, felt or spotted a ghost, ask around to see if anyone else has had the same experience. If you start getting too spooked just say "Spirit, I release you!" and turn on the lights. Compare notes with your friends to see if you have experienced a well-known spook!

SERIOUS SPOOKS!

Edinburgh, Scotland
The famous Edinburgh playhouse has a friendly ghost called Albert who wears a grey coat. He's believed to be an old stagehand who can't resist helping out now and then!

Banghar Fort, India
People say a wizard put a curse on this Indian village, and soon after that, the place was invaded. To this day, people there think that the ghosts keep nosy visitors away.

The Charles Bridge, Prague
In the middle ages, ten Lords were beheaded on the bridge. Their ghosts still linger on there, singing in the night to scare off anyone who dares to cross the bridge.

SAFTEY FIRST!

Remember to always tell an adult where you're going and never go out alone at night.

WHY NOT?
Bring along a camera, and see if you can capture any spooky goings-on on film!

DONE!

DATE COMPLETED

87 PRINT A BLOCK PICTURE

The next time your meal comes in a polystyrene box, make sure to keep hold of it. You can use it to make a cool piece of art!

YOU WILL NEED:

- Leftover food container
- Pencil
- Plate
- Poster paint
- Paper
- Paint roller

1 Lightly sketch out your design on one of the flat sides of your food box. When you are happy with it, press harder with your pencil to leave an imprint.

2 Put your paint on your plate and dip your roller into it. Make sure all the roller wheel is lightly and evenly covered in paint.

3 Roll the paint onto the lunch box, making sure you have covered the whole surface. Try not to put the paint on too thickly, or your design won't show.

4 Press a sheet of paper onto the painted box. Rub over it gently with your palm so that the paint spreads evenly.

5 Peel the paper off to reveal your art! You can repeat this many times to make things like posters, wrapping paper, or even to decorate workbooks!

WHY NOT?
Use different colours on your stencil and layer them on to the page.

DONE!

DATE COMPLETED

88 BE A HUMAN LIE DETECTOR

Follow these top tips to uncover un-truths!

BODY LANGUAGE CHECKLIST:

Read their body language! Check out these classic liar's tell-all traits.

- ✓ **Touching the face**
- ✓ **Rubbing the back of neck**
- ✓ **Playing with hair**
- ✓ **Blinking more than usual**
- ✓ **Wringing their hands**
- ✓ **Not looking directly at you**

OTHER SIGNS TO LOOK OUT FOR:

Note their tone of voice. Do they look happy when they're talking about something sad? Are they nodding but saying no?

Are they too still? If a liar is smart, they might try and stay still to avoid looking shifty. If you notice they aren't moving, or that they're talking in one tone of voice, then they could be up to no good!

DONE!   DATE COMPLETED

MEASURE RAINFALL {89}

You don't need lots of expensive equipment to learn about the weather. Try making a simple rain gauge, and start keeping track of rainfall in your area.

1 Cut the top of an empty 2 litre drinks bottle and weigh it down with some stones at the bottom. Flip the top section upside down and pop it back inside to make a funnel.

2 Mark a scale in centimeters on the side of your gauge using a waterproof marker and a ruler.

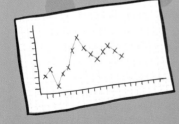

3 Write down the amount of rainfall you see on a graph, or a simple chart. Mark the days of the week along the bottom axis, and write the amount of rainfall along the side axis.

WHY NOT?
Ask a friend or relative to also keep track of rainfall where they live and then compare notes!

DONE! DATE COMPLETED

90 DESIGN A COAT OF ARMS

A traditional coat of arms is a decorated shield that features all kinds of things related to your family. Have a go at making your very own!

1 First, draw a basic shape for your coat of arms. The most common shapes are shown above, or you can design your own!

2 Write a list of words that spring to mind when you think about your family. These will make up symbols of your shield! Write down the name of each family member and something cool about them.

3 Split your coat of arms into sections, one for each member of your family. Now take one thing about them from your list and draw it into that section.

WHY NOT?
Add a family motto to your coat of arms. E.g. Friday night is movie night!

DONE! DATE COMPLETED

SPIN A BASKETBALL ON YOUR FINGERTIP

Practice makes perfect with this tricky skill, but soon you'll impress everyone with your spinning style!

1 Holding the basketball in one hand, take the opposite hand and spin the ball, fast. Use any of the fingers on that hand to hold up the ball as it spins, but your index finger might be the easiest.

2 Gently pat the ball on the side as you spin it on the pad of your index finger. Wait for one second, and then spin again.

3 Keep your elbows bent and tuck your chin under so you remain steady. Try to lengthen the spin each time!

TOP TIP!
Deflate the ball slightly before you begin. This will create a larger surface area when you touch the ball, and will help you to control it better!

DONE!   DATE COMPLETED

92 MAKE A RECYCLED BIRDHOUSE

Looking for birds in your backyard? Encourage winged visitors to stop by for a rest, or a snack!

YOU WILL NEED:

- Empty, clean cardboard juice carton
- Paint and paintbrush
- Scissors
- Glue
- Hole punch
- Lollipop stick
- Bird seed

1 Paint and decorate the outside of the carton and let it dry.

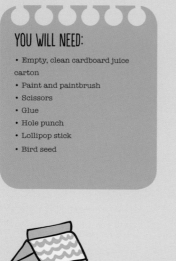

2 Carefully, cut a rectangle in the bottom of the carton for your birds to pop in and out of!

3 Take your lollipop stick, and glue it to the bottom of your carton. This will make a perch for your birds to land on!

4 Punch a hole in the top of your carton, and feed some strong string through the hole.

5 Fill the bottom of the carton with bird seed and hang it from the branch of a tree. Watch as the hungry birds come to visit!

WHY NOT?
Keep a diary of all the different types of birds that visit your garden!

DONE!   DATE COMPLETED

93 BUILD AN EXTREME INDOOR DEN

What's better on a rainy day than a super-sized, homemade den? Gather together blankets, cushions and chairs to see what you could make!

Put all breakable objects away. Try not to use weak or small pieces of furniture that might fall down on the people inside the den.

Drape blankets, sheets and towels over large pieces of furniture like a dining table, or the back of an armchair, or sofa.

Use chairs to prop up your sheets, too. Turn them around so they can be used as tables inside the den.

Sheets make the best roofs because they are light. Keep them in place with bulldog clips or cushions.

Fill your den with fun things to do. Books, games and snacks are perfect!

The inside of your den must be comfy and cosy. Fill the floor with cushions so you've always got somewhere squishy to sit.

DONE!   DATE COMPLETED

NEVER BE BORED AGAIN 94

If you're alone, there's no reason to be bored! Even when you're all by yourself, there is always something fun to try.

1 Bounce and hit a tennis ball against a wall. How many times can you hit it in a row?

2 Twirl a hula hoop indoors or out. How long can you keep it spinning without dropping it?

3 Make up a dance routine to your favourite song.

4 Find three things in your bedroom that could be used to make instruments.

5 Create a small shadow puppet theatre using a box, a torch and some small toy figures.

6 Find a book you've never read before and start it.

7 Write a letter to yourself in the future.

8 Invent and draw your own comic book character.

DONE!   DATE COMPLETED

95 MAKE HOMEMADE LEMONADE

What could be better than a glass of cool, homemade lemondade on a hot Summer day? This recipe makes enough for six glasses.

YOU WILL NEED:

- 8 lemons
- 1.5 litres (2.5 pints) of water
- 250g (8oz) of sugar

1 Squeeze the juice of eight lemons into a jug - make sure you take out any pips!

2 Ask an adult to heat a thrid of the water in a pan with the sugar. Make sure to keep stirring until the sugar has completly dissolved, then mix with the lemon juice.

3 Add the rest of the water to the jug, then leave in the fridge to chill. Serve with ice and a slice of lemon.

DONE!   DATE COMPLETED

TRANSFER TRICKS

Try this cool trick to see how the energy from one falling ball can be transfered in to another.

1 For this experiment you will need a basketball (or something similar, like a football) and a tennis ball.

2 Hold the tennis ball over the basketball, and drop both at the same time.

WHY NOT?
Try adding a ping pong ball to see if you can get the trick to work with three balls?

3 The basketball should stop, but the tennis ball should launch itself upwards as the energy from the basketball transfers in to it.

DONE!   DATE COMPLETED

97 MASTER THE ART OF ORIGAMI

Origami is the ancient Japanese art of paper folding. You'll be amazed at what you can make from just a simple square of paper. Why not start by making this cute rabbit?

1 Take a square of paper and fold it in half, diagonally.

2 Open the paper out, then fold the corners inward towards the centre fold.

3 Fold down the top corner to make a triangle.

4 Fold the tip of the top flap back to make the tail.

5 Fold in half along the center fold.

6 Your paper should now look like this.

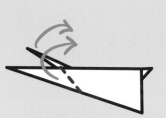

7 Use scissors to make a small cut a third of the way along the centre fold. This will make the rabbit's ears.

8 Next, bend back each of the ears.

9 Fold the bottom corners under. This will make your rabbit sit up.

10 Fold the ears down. You now have your very own origami rabbit!

WHY NOT?
Try using different coloured paper and draw some details on your new creation!

DONE!

DATE COMPLETED

98 PLAY WATER BALLOON VOLLEYBALL

This is the perfect game to play on a hot day at the beach, in the park, or even in your back garden. But watch out - you're going to get wet!

1 Set up your net, and gather together your players. You'll need at least four people to play this game.

2 Get a pile of water balloons ready.

3 Each team grabs a beach towel or blanket, and uses it to launch a balloon over the net for the other team, who have to try and catch it in their towel. The winning team is the one that bursts the fewest balloons (and stays the driest!).

WHY NOT?
Double the fun, and try playing with two water balloons at the same time!

DONE! | DATE COMPLETED

Boomerangs are throwing sticks traditionally used by Australian Aboriginals. Try making this cool three winged version from a simple sheet of card.

1 Take a sheet of thin card and copy the basic shape below onto it.

2 Cut out the shape and fold down each of the three edges along the dotted line.

3 To throw your boomerang, hold it by one of the wings with the unfolded edge facing forwards. Bring your arm forward in a swinging motion, and let go. Then wait for it to come back!

DONE!

DATE COMPLETED

FIND YOUR CHINESE ZODIAC ANIMAL

The Chinese Zodiac is ancient, but it is just as meaningful today! Look up the year you were born – which animal are you?

RAT

2008, 1996, 1984, 1972

Your intelligence makes you a great speaker, and you have a very busy social life.

OX

2009, 1997, 1985, 1973

You are strong, steady, and reliable. But most importantly, you have loads of patience.

TIGER

2010, 1998, 1986, 1974

Ambition and confidence make you a great leader. You are also brave and generous!

RABBIT

2011, 1999, 1987, 1975

You are strong willed, elegant and kindly - and you hate having disagreements!

DRAGON

2012, 2000, 1988, 1976

You have an A+ imagination and like to meet all of your goals.

SNAKE

2013, 2001, 1989, 1977

You are a super organized communicator who likes to think serious thoughts.

HORSE

2002, 1990, 1978, 1966

You work very hard, but are always up for a wild, warm-hearted adventure.

RAM

2015, 2003, 1991, 1979

You stay calm - even in a crisis. You are always generous, too!

MONKEY

2016, 2004, 1992, 1980,

You have a bright wit and know how to turn on the charm. You're always on the go!

ROOSTER

2017, 2005, 1993, 1981

You are very dignified, and usually love to be the focus of attention! You are also generous and well-meaning.

DOG

2018, 2006, 1994, 1982

You seem to have a lot of luck! You're also honest and wise beyond your years..

PIG

2019, 2007, 1995, 1983

Your determination and spirit helps others. You always know how to stay positive.

DONE! DATE COMPLETED

101 MAKE A PAPIER MÂCHÉ BOWL

Follow these simple steps to transform old newspapers into these colourful bowls. Why not make one as a gift for a friend?

YOU WILL NEED:

- A bowl to use as a mould
- Cling film
- Newspapers cut into strips
- PVA glue mixed with water
- Scissors
- Paints and a paintbrush
- Clear varnish

1 Cover a bowl with clingfilm. The clingfilm will stop the papier mâché sticking to the bowl once it's dried.

2 Start by brushing the newspaper strips with the watered down PVA glue and overlapping them on the outside of the bowl.

3 Once you've covered the bowl in newspaper, leave it to dry for a couple of hours before adding another layer. Make sure they aren't too wet or they won't dry flat.

4 After you've built up a few layers of paper, allow them to dry out completely before removing the papier mâché from the mould. Trim the edges with scissors.

5 Now it's time to decorate your creation! You can use paint, glitter or even add on a few more layers of coloured paper for a cool collage effect.

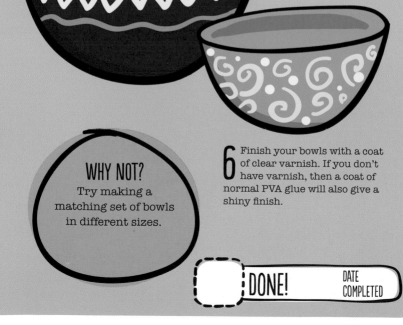

WHY NOT?
Try making a matching set of bowls in different sizes.

6 Finish your bowls with a coat of clear varnish. If you don't have varnish, then a coat of normal PVA glue will also give a shiny finish.

DONE!

DATE COMPLETED

STAYING SAFE:
DOS AND DON'TS

 DO: Take care while using scissors, and other sharp objects.

DO: Wear a helmet while riding a bike or a skateboard.

DO: Always wear old clothes or an apron when doing art projects.

DO: Carefully follow the instructions and pay attention to any safety warnings.

 DON'T: Start a messy project without asking an adult.

DON'T: Go anywhere without telling an adult, first!

ACKNOWLEDGEMENTS

Written by Laura Dower
Editors: Alexandra Koken, Gemma Barder and Fay Evans
Design and illustration: Dan Bramall and Katie Knutton

Elements of illustration for activities 38, 41, 55 and 61, 64, 96 and 100 from Shutterstock.